DATE DUE

JAN 16 '73			
MAR 15 '77			
DEC 28 '77			
OCT 1 1979			
JAN 8 '81			
5 J			
APR 15 '91			
APR 22 '91			
MAY 2 '91			
APR 15 '92			
APR 5 '93			
FEB 3 '95			

Whence these stories?
Whence these legends and traditions,
With their frequent repetitions,
And their wild reverberations,
As of thunder in the mountains?

Thunder

IN THE MOUNTAINS

Legends of Canada

BY

HILDA MARY HOOKE

ILLUSTRATED BY CLARE BICE

Oxford University Press

TORONTO

First published   1947
Seventh impression   1969

Printed in Canada
by
JOHN DEYELL LIMITED

TO SMITHY

WITH LOVE

Ye who love a nation's legends,
Love the ballads of a people,
That like voices from afar off
Call to us to pause and listen,
Speak in tones so plain and childlike . . .
Ye whose hearts are fresh and simple,
Who have faith in God and Nature,
Who believe that in all ages
Every human heart is human,
That in even savage bosoms
There are longings, yearnings, strivings
For the good they comprehend not—
Listen to these wild traditions,
Full of hope, and yet of heartbreak,
Full of all the tender pathos
Of the Here and the Hereafter!
                    —The Song of Hiawatha

Preface

These stories are based upon legends gathered up in a variety of ways. Some are taken from authentic source material such as the Anthropological Series issued by the Canadian Department of Mines; others embody parts of legendary cycles which are to be found in varying forms among the Indian tribes, such as the Hiawatha, Glooskap, and Nanna-Bijou stories; some, like the Legend of the Wishing Well, were picked up by word of mouth, and some were adapted from existing versions of familiar legends, as the stories of Cadieux and Qu'Appelle.

The stories have been treated freely, and I have tried to retain the simplicity of folk-lore language. I find it very fascinating to believe that all legendry and mythology is built on a basic thread of truth; that great and godlike forms did appear in the childhood of the world, and that the powers of good and evil sometimes strive in visible manifestations for the domination of mankind. For this reason I have chosen only those legends that seem to me to contain an element of such truth, or to illustrate in a fresh and appealing way the minds who conceived them.

All printed source material is included in the bibliography, and I am also indebted to the Reference Department staff of the London Public Library for allowing me access to clippings and newspaper articles, and for much patience and help in tracking down stories.

H. M. H.

Contents

Thunder

IN THE MOUNTAINS

The Garden of Gitche Manitou

*Long, long ago, when the world was very new, the Great
Spirit sat and thought over the things that he had made.
There were a great many of them, places and creatures and
people, and already they were setting about their own
affairs. The Great Spirit sat watching them.*

"I have made a very busy world," he said to himself.

*Time went by, and the things and the people got busier
and busier. The noise they made came right into the place
where the Great Spirit lived, and disturbed him at his
thinking.*

*"I shall never get any work done at this rate," said the
Great Spirit. "I must have a place where I can think as I
please."*

*He told the people they must be quiet, for he was going
to do some more creating. So the sun stopped shining and
the wind stopped blowing, and over all the world there was
silence; and the Great Spirit created.*

*He created a garden, and it was larger than any garden
he had made before. It lay between two seas, and in it were
rocks and mountains, lakes and rivers, plains and forests.
It contained every kind of living creature, and there was
rain, and snow, and sunshine; last of all there were people,*

simple, childish people, who scraped the soil and caught fish in the rivers and game in the forests, and went about their business quietly and happily. The Great Spirit walked among them, and they called him Gitche Manitou, the Great One. He was their father, they looked to him for food and heat and clothing; and he gave them everything in abundance.

And the Great Spirit said:

"This is my garden; here I will think new thoughts, and rest when I am weary."

Then the world went on as before; and between the two seas a great country grew and became a nation; and it was called Canada.

But it was still the Garden of Gitche Manitou.

4

How the Animals Got
Their Fur Coats

You have heard of the Great White Country to the north, where all the animals wear fur coats and the people wrap themselves in skins and blankets to keep warm. Perhaps you live in one of those lands yourself, where the winters are long and very cold, and you tuck your ears and fingers and toes into woolly things so that they won't get frost-bitten.

The place I am thinking of is where the prairies of

Manitoba stretch northward until they break into a wild country of lakes and rivers, swamps and forests, leading at last to Hudson's Bay. The people who lived along the west coast of the Bay were called Swampy Crees, because they built their homes in the swamps and marshes instead of staying on the plains below; and they still tell stories to their children about the days when Wesukechak, the Friend of Gitche Manitou the Great Spirit, lived among men. It is one of these tales that I am going to tell you.

Wesukechak was the Big Man of the Crees, just as Glooskap was the Big Man of the Micmacs, and Nanna-Bijou of the Ojibways, and Hiawatha of the Iroquois. Perhaps in the mind of the Great Spirit they were all the same person. We don't know. But the people of these early days got sick and bothered and miserable, just as we do, and needed someone to pick them up and put them to rights and show them what to do next; so this is what Wesukechak did, and he did it for all living creatures.

Now there was a time when all the animals dressed alike. Instead of the beautiful fur wraps that they have today, they wore plain grey coats, and they had no horns nor other ornaments. They didn't think much about it except in winter, and then the cruel north-east winds blowing from the ice-blocks beyond the Bay cut through their thin coats like knives, and they hid in holes and caves and hated to come out even to look for food.

One day, when snow was piled high across the marsh country and frost crackled like gunfire through the forests, Muskwa the Bear called the animals in council.

6

"Brothers," said he, "we have suffered long enough. Surely the Gitche Manitou does not know how cold it is up here; our coats are much too thin. Don't you think we should ask for warmer ones?"

Wapoos the Rabbit said:

"O Muskwa, the idea is a good one. But hadn't we better get Wesukechak, the Big Chief, to ask for us? It is a hard thing to talk to the Gitche Manitou, and we so small and far away. He might not hear us."

The animals agreed with this; so they chose Muskwa the Bear, Kakwa the Porcupine, and Atik the Deer to carry their message to the Big Chief Wesukechak.

Wesukechak listened to the three animals, and then he said that it would all depend on what Gitche Manitou, the Great One, thought about it.

"You must leave the matter with me," he said, "and when it is settled I will let you know."

Atik the Deer spoke up timidly:

"Do you think that we might ask for horns as well? I have always wanted horns—they could be made very cheaply. Just little ones would do."

Wesukechak said he would see what could be done about the horns. The animals went home and told the others what the Big Chief had said; and they all sat down very patiently in their holes and caves to wait for Gitche Manitou.

The next day Wesukechak went away; he went a long distance, and then he climbed a high mountain and sat on the top of it, and after a time the Great Spirit came and spoke to him. For three days Wesukechak sat listening; and all the time he spoke not one word.

But when he came down from the mountain and got home again he called the three animals, Muskwa, Kakwa, and Atik; and when they came to him he was smiling.

"You are to have the coats, little brothers," said Wesuke-chak, "and I am to make them. The Gitche Manitou is glad because you asked him, and you are to choose, each of you, the kind of coat you want."

The three were very happy, and they thanked Wesuke-chak and wagged their tails with joy. But Atik looked a bit anxious, and when the others were not looking he pulled the Big Chief's sleeve and whispered:

"Was anything said about horns, O Wesukechak?"

Wesukechak said quite softly, so that Muskwa and Kakwa did not hear:

"When you come for your coat, look underneath my work-table. You will find a package with your name on it."

Muskwa, Kakwa, and Atik hurried back to their friends with the good news. Muskwa got on a big rock and made a speech, and all the animals gathered round to hear him.

"O brothers," he said, "the Gitche Manitou has been very kind. Not only does he give us our coats, but we may choose whatever pattern and colour we like. This is most generous, and we must show that we are grateful. Make out your orders at once. Wesukechak, the Big Chief, will make the coats, and by autumn they will be ready."

You can imagine the excitement and bustle that went on after that. Everybody talked at once. Wapoos the Rabbit, being handy with his paws, had to make out the orders, and

8

if his ears had not been long ones he would never have got them down properly, with each animal trying to shout louder than the others so that his order would be heard. There was so much noise that the birds came to see what was happening, and when they heard about it they were annoyed and said to one another:

"Why didn't we think of that? We need new clothes too. Something must be done about it."

So they flew off and held a council together; and what they did you will see in another story.

At last the orders were finished, and Wapoos gave them to Muskwa.

"There you are," said he. "For goodness' sake be off with them. I'm going to have a sleep."

And he went into his burrow and did not come out for seven days.

Now there was only one animal who did not order his coat, and that was Mooswa, the great bull Moose. Mooswa was a sleepy, soft creature, and his greatest joy in life was eating; he loved the juicy roots of the water-lilies that grew in the swamps, and the honey-sweet leaves of young trees. Eating, of course, is a very pleasant thing; but if you do too much of it you soon forget what else goes on in the world. This was what Mooswa did. On the day the coat orders were given he was down in the river-bed eating water-lily roots, and knew nothing about it till Nehkik the Otter stuck his head out of the water and called to him.

"What kind of coat did you order, brother?"

Mooswa lifted his nose, all dripping with juice, and shook the water out of his eyes.

"Coat?" said he in his sleepy voice. "What coat?"

Then Nehkik laughed, for he knew Mooswa well.

"O greedy one," he said, "while you were eating your dinner we ordered our new coats. You'll have to hurry if you want one, for Atik the deer is carrying the orders to the Big Chief's workshop."

Mooswa came out of the river-bed quickly, and went as fast as he could to Atik's house; but the Deer was already on his way.

"Oh well," said Mooswa, who never bothered about anything very long, "I daresay the Big Chief will have some extra coats. I shall get there in good time when they are ready, so that I can choose a handsome one."

And he went back to the river-bed to have supper.

The summer went very slowly for the animals, because they thought so much about their coats and spent hours wondering what they would be like. No one had seen Wesukechak; he had shut himself in his workshop, and a sign hung outside: "NOT TO BE DISTURBED." So the animals crept past on tiptoe, and even the birds arranged to sing matins and evensong in another place.

By and by the hot dry days of summer melted into the crisp, misty days of September; nights grew cold, and the animals covered themselves with dried grasses and leaves to keep warm while they slept. Atik the Deer and Maheekun the Grey Wolf kept a sharp look-out at the workshop, for it was autumn now, and surely the coats would soon be ready.

One morning when frost lay like silver icing upon the ground, Maheekun came padding along the path by the workshop. He looked at the workshop as he went past, and then he stopped, rubbed his eyes, and looked again. The sign was gone—and in the open door stood the Big Chief, smiling and waving his hand.

That day, as the frost melted under the noontide sun and birds on their way south stopped to watch what was going on, the animals came in procession to Wesukechak's workshop. They were quite quiet and solemn, for they had looked forward to the new coats so long that now they were almost afraid to see them. Suppose they were not wonderful after all; suppose they were just plain ordinary coats . . .

Then Wesukechak threw the door of the workshop wide open, and the animals at the front went in. There were the coats, laid in fluffy piles on the workshop shelves. They were soft and sleek and furry, they gleamed and shone like sunlight, white and gold and tawny, red and rust and ebony black; there were striped ones and spotted ones, polka dots and plain colours; but they were all beautiful, and when you touched them they felt like warm velvet.

And now there was plenty of excitement. The animals forgot their fear and crowded into the workshop so fast that the Big Chief had to call Muskwa and Atik to help him. One by one each animal's coat was found and given to him, and he was sent outside to try it on in front of a pool where he could see himself in his new finery. Each screamed to his neighbour to look, and although no one looked at anybody but himself they were all very happy.

Such handsome creatures they were! Wapoos had a fur robe as white as a snowdrift; Pisseu the Lynx had a coat of butter-yellow, with little tufted ear-muffs; while Kakwa the

Porcupine, who wanted to be different, walked proudly up and down in a quilled coat of mail that clanked with every step he took. And who can describe the glory of Atik, whose coat was pale cream-buff with dark brown shadows, and upon whose head was fastened a crown of wonderful horns, branched and pointed like bronze candlesticks; or Sakwaseu the Mink whose furs were so beautiful that the little animal was quite overcome, and sat down by the pool and cried?

At last everyone was fitted, and Wesukechak stood in the workshop doorway.

"Go home, my children," he said to the animals. "Enjoy yourselves and be happy, but remember one thing. Because you are better to look at you must be better yourselves. It is no good having fine clothes and being ugly and mean and greedy inside. Line your new coats with kind deeds and gentle thoughts, and they will protect you from evil things."

The animals bowed their heads to the Big Chief and thanked him for his words and for all the work he had done for them; and they went away to their homes. Now the path from the workshop led through the willow swamp. There stood Mooswa, eating water-lily roots. When he saw the animals coming along in their new coats he thought that he had died and gone to Heaven.

"Surely these are angel-creatures," he said to himself. "One of them has a crown on his head, and one is dressed in cloth of gold. Perhaps they have brought a robe for me."

And he hurried to meet them.

But when Kakwa the Porcupine saw Mooswa he shouted with laughter.

"Look," he cried to the others, "here's Fatty, still in his old suit!"

All the animals stopped on the river-bank and laughed at Mooswa. They pointed at his old grey coat and said all kinds of rude things to him, till poor Mooswa, seeing that they were not angels but his own brothers, began to weep great sticky tears and went blundering off to beg Wesukechak for a new coat.

Wesukechak listened to him and then said:

"I have no coat for you, my brother Mooswa. You gave me no order, so I thought you did not want one."

Mooswa was more upset than ever, and said between sobs:

"O Big Chief, I was idle and greedy, and I forgot to order my coat till it was too late. Now I am laughed at by all my friends, and my life is not worth living. Give me a coat or let me die, for even my water-lily roots have lost their sweetness."

Wesukechak was sorry for the Moose, but he said there was nothing he could do. Then he turned and looked into the workshop.

"There is a piece of cloth left here," he said. "You could have that. It won't fit very well, but I can stitch it here and there so that it will stay on, and at least it will be warm."

Mooswa's tears fell faster, for the cloth was dull coloured and harsh to touch.

13

"Isn't there one little piece of golden cloth left, O Wesukechak? One tiny patch, one thread even, so that I shall not be disgraced in the sight of my friends?"

But there was not even one thread.

So Wesukechak threw the brown cloth over Mooswa's shoulders, and he pulled it here and pinned it there and did what he could with it; but it was too big in some places and too small in others, so that it hung in awkward folds and did not fit at the neck at all. When it was fastened on, Wesukechak said kindly:

"I have remembered one more thing, brother Mooswa. There is an extra pair of horns that no one else wanted; you may have those."

Mooswa put the horns on, and cheered up a little, for they were heavy, large things that at least looked important.

"They are bigger than Atik's," said he, and went to the pool to look at himself. The coat was a little queer, but not so bad when you got used to it; and the horns were tremendous things, branching out like the boughs of the great balsam trees. Mooswa went away quite comforted; but when he got home the other animals laughed harder than ever, and asked if he was going to carry those tree trunks about with him for the rest of his life.

So Mooswa took to living by himself, going out to feed in lonely places; and so you will find him today.

And did the animals remember what the Big Chief had told them, and become gentle and kind? I am afraid they did not; for they were so proud of their grand clothes that they grew sharp and jealous and unpleasant with each other. Indeed, many of them never spoke to one another from that day forward, and don't now as far as I know.

Then the Gitche Manitou said they must have no more new clothes until they had learned to behave themselves; and when that will be nobody can say. But the Gitche Manitou knows.

How the Birds Got Their Colours

You will remember that when Wesukechak the Big Chief made new coats for the animals, there was a great deal of chatter amongst the Birds. They were sharp little creatures, and they saw that smart clothes were going to make the animals snobbish and hard to deal with.

"Think of something," they said to Hoohoomisseu, the Owl. "You are wise, you can see in the dark. Tell us what to do."

So the Owl sat and thought for three nights and a day; and then he called the Birds together and said:

"Brothers, I have an idea."

The Birds flapped their wings and cried:

"Say on, O Hoohoomisseu!"

And Hoohoomisseu said:

"The animals asked for new coats because they were cold. We can go away when winter comes, so that we don't need fur robes; but don't you think these white dresses are rather uninteresting? I must say I should like a little colour myself. How would it be if we asked the Gitche Manitou's permission to have our coats painted?"

Now the birds had always worn white dresses, just as the animals wore grey, and no one had been discontented. But now they looked at one another and said:

"How pale and washed-out we look! How dull to be all dressed alike! You are right, Hoohoomisseu, we must move with the times. Let us have our coats painted at once."

Seeseep the Duck, Keyask the Gull, and Hoohoomisseu the Owl were chosen to act as messengers, and again Wesukechak was asked to present their request to the Gitche Manitou. The Big Chief received the birds kindly, for he had been expecting them.

"Well, my little brothers," he said when he had heard their story, "and who do you think is going to paint these gay dresses for you?"

The Birds looked at one another, and Seeseep gave Keyask a poke and Keyask nudged Hoohoomisseu. Hoohoomisseu said timidly:

"We thought perhaps *you* would have time to do it for us, O Wesukechak."

18

Then the Big Chief laughed and he said:

"I have worked all the summer to make coats for the animals, and now you want me to work all the winter as well. Do I get no rest, thoughtless ones?"

The Birds hung their heads; but they took courage, for there was a twinkle in the Big Chief's eye, and his voice was friendly.

"Go home, my little ones," he said. "When I am not too busy I will see what can be done. Then we will talk again."

So the Birds went home, hoping the Big Chief would not be busy long.

Then Wesukechak climbed to the high mountain-top where he always went to listen to the Great Spirit; and he sat there and looked down upon the plains and rivers and forests stretched below, and up to the soft clouds that rolled above his head; and he said:

"Great Father, the world is very beautiful."

And the Gitche Manitou came and stood on the mountain beside Wesukechak; and he said:

"What do you ask for, my son?"

Wesukechak bowed his head and answered:

"Great Father, because the world is beautiful the little children of the air are not content. They wish to be beautiful too."

The Gitche Manitou said:

"Is it not enough that I paint the clouds at sunrise and colour the flowers in summer and the leaves at the fall of the year? Do they wish to dip their wings in the rainbow and wear the rays of the sun upon their heads?"

Wesukechak answered humbly:

"They are very small, Great Father."

The Gitche Manitou looked down into the forests, and there were the birds sitting among the branches.

"I had forgotten how small they were," said the Gitche Manitou. "Make whatever arrangements you like about it."

And Wesukechak went home with a warm feeling around his middle, because the birds were to have their coats painted.

All that winter, while the icebergs glittered like spun glass in the bay and long blue shadows of leafless trees lay across the blinding glare of the snow, the Big Chief sat in his workshop making paints. He boiled roots and poured the boiling water into kettles; he squeezed the juice from berries and pounded precious stones into powder; he put a little of this into a little of that, and shook them all up together; he emptied the whole mess into a great kettle and stewed it over the fire for days at a time. You could smell the boiling paint for miles, and the animals walking by in their new fur coats held their noses and said to one another:

"What dreadful soup the Big Chief eats for his supper!"

Long before the ice-packs had melted in the bay or the buds had grown soft on the pussy willows, the birds came tumbling back from their winter homes in the south. The weather was cold and stormy, and they got their feet frost-nipped and caught colds in their heads; but they felt it was best to be on hand when the Big Chief was ready, and who could tell when that might be?

One morning the birds were aroused by Opihpihcheew the Robin who was a wide-awake fellow and always knew what was going on.

"Quick," said he, "get up. The sun is shining, and we are all wanted at the Big Chief's workshop."

You can imagine how fast the birds scrambled off their sleeping porches and got themselves ready. Dressing was a hasty affair, a peck here and a dab there, and without waiting for breakfast they hurried off to the big wood where the Chief was waiting for them.

There were the paint-pots standing in neat rows on the workshop table, and beside them were brushes of all kinds and sizes with shining new bristles.

"Look at the colours!" cried someone, and all the birds crowded round to see. Each paint-pot had a bright label pasted around its waist; very gay they were, each pot painted in its own colour and having its name in big black letters on its label: NOON-DAY BLUE, SUNSET RED, STARDUST, MOON-GOLD, THUNDERBOLT PURPLE, and so on.

And now Wesukechak had his work cut out, for every bird began screaming at the top of his voice for the colours he wanted.

"Blue wings!" shrieked somebody.

"Green legs!" cried another; and they all clamoured together until the greenwood shook and trembled with the uproar.

Then Wesukechak the Big Chief stood up and raised his voice, and it boomed over the shrill piping of the birds like a great bell.

21

"Silence!" said the Big Chief; and over the greenwood stillness dropped like a mantle of snow. Every little bird-face turned towards the master, and restless feet stood quietly. Wesukechak took up his brushes.

"Stand before me in order," he commanded; and each bird in turn stood before the workshop table and received his colours. The Big Chief worked swiftly, dipping his brushes into the pots, mixing and smoothing, with a streak here and a blob there, until he had the colours he wanted. As the birds were finished they moved out into an open clearing, where they sat and dried in the sun. How brightly their feathers flashed as they spread their wings to the wind! Each bird had what he asked for, so there were some very queer arrangements; but as the Big Chief took the colours on his palette they seemed to change, to grow soft and melt into one another, so that they looked as natural together as the colours of the rainbow.

Seeseep the Duck, for instance, had a willow-green head, wings of twilight blue, earth-brown back, breast feathers of mist grey, and legs dipped in sunset red. You might look very queer indeed if you wore a suit like that; but as the colours dripped from the Big Chief's brush, each one ran a little bit into the next, so that you couldn't tell where one ended and another began. At all events, Seeseep was quite satisfied, and lay contentedly on the ground with his wings spread out so that they might dry more quickly.

"Look at me!" piped Opihpihcheew the Robin. "Isn't this the finest waistcoat you've ever seen?"

Indeed it was a grand affair—warm rosy red like the glow of the sky at sunrise; and with it Opihpihcheew wore a jaunty black cap and a coat of soft brown. Before Seeseep and Opihpihcheew had finished admiring one another, Keyask the Gull came swaggering by, gaudy in blue and yellow.

"Do you want to hear a good joke?" said he. "Look down yonder. Paspaschao the Sapsucker went out on a party this morning—and now there's no paint left for him!"

Now Paspaschao was the kind of person who knew everybody and went everywhere; he was a gay jolly fellow, full of jokes and stories, but you could never depend on him in springtime because of his love for the sweet, rich sap that rose in the trees. From early morning till nightfall he went tap-tapping, tap-tapping, drawing out long, delicious beakfuls, until the stuff went to his head, and he hit himself against the trees because he couldn't fly straight—which, of course, was a very foolish thing to do.

This morning Paspaschao had been at his old tricks; he had got up very early and gone out for a drink, and so had missed Opihpihcheew's message. Later on, when he was sitting in a tree near the Big Chief's workshop, feeling a little bit dizzy, he looked out and saw several of his mates flying past.

"Good gracious!" said Paspaschao, rubbing his eyes. "That sap must be getting rather strong. I suppose I shouldn't have taken so much before breakfast."

He looked again and began to get frightened, for instead of white birds flying he saw every colour under the sun. (Certainly that sap was altogether too strong.)

Then Paspaschao remembered. The Big Chief's paint-pots!

23

Through the woods went the Sapsucker, bumping into tree-trunks and bruising himself dreadfully, so that by the time he got to the workshop one eye was black and blue and he limped in one wing; but he had no time to think about it, for there was the Big Chief washing his brushes, and behind him stood a row of empty paint-pots.

Paspaschao cried out:

"Where are my colours, O Wesukechak?"

And the Big Chief answered:

"There are no colours left, my brother Papaschao. When you did not come with the others I thought you did not wish to be painted, so I saved nothing for you."

Then Paspaschao wept bitterly, and he said:

"O Wesukechak, shall my head burn with shame and my days end in misery? Is there not one tiny scraping left, one bright drop to change this dreadful whiteness?"

Wesukechak looked in all the pots, even turned them upside down; but there was not one tiny scraping. Then the Big Chief said:

"My little brother, you cannot have your sap and drink it too. Either you must wear your old white suit for the rest of your life, or you must beg mercy of your brothers. Perhaps one of them will share his coat with you."

The tears of Paspaschao rolled down his white feathers and fell drip, drip, on the pine-needles of the forest; for he felt sure no one would want to give up any of his fine new clothes. He cried so hard that he did not hear Opihpihcheew flying down, with Keyask and Seeseep behind him.

"We'll help you, Paspaschao," said Opihpihcheew. "Dry your eyes. You shall have the gayest coat of us all."

24

Down trooped the rest of the birds, and from each of them the Big Chief took a brushful of colour for Paspaschao. Opihpihcheew gave some red from his waistcoat, and Paspaschao got a red cap and bib out of it; Keyask gave his yellow for his vest, and Mokwa the Loon some black bars for his hood and wings. Soon, as Opihpihcheew had said, the coat of Paspaschao was the brightest of them all.

"There you are, my son," said the Big Chief. "But don't forget you owe your finery to the generosity of your friends." To the others he said:

"Go in peace, little brothers. Let your happiness bring pleasure to all the world; and remember that the gay colours you wear were not of my making, but a gift from the Great Spirit."

So the birds flew homeward, and as they went, Paspaschao said to Keyask:

"Let everyone come to my house in the poplar grove and we will have a feast. You look after the invitations and I will provide the refreshments."

Keyask did as he was asked, and that afternoon there was great merriment in the poplar grove. Paspaschao had a wonderful spread of fat insects and juicy worms. He had worked all day collecting sap and had not touched a drop himself; moreover, from that day on he got drunk no more, because, said he: "Since my brothers gave up their colours to make my coat, I can give up making an idiot of myself while I wear it."

That evening when the feast was over the birds flew to the highest tree-tops and sang to the Great Spirit. Sweeter

25

music it was than they had ever made before because of their thankful hearts; and more sweetly than any of them sang Paspaschao.

And the Great Spirit, listening, smiled.

Glooskap's Beads

Were you born in Nova Scotia, the little country that pushes its nose out to sea and takes the full force of the Atlantic Ocean in its face? If you were, I needn't tell you how the salt wind sweeps in from the open sea and roars up the Bay of Fundy; how the spray hisses over the rocks of Cap D'Or when the tide comes crashing in, and how Blomidon wears his purple robe at twilight when Fish-Hawk rises over the Cumberland hills.

But if you come from the west or the north, or up from the big country to the south, then I will tell you a story of Glooskap, who lived on Blomidon long years ago; and our cousins from Nova Scotia shall listen and tell us if we go wrong, for I expect they know the story better than we do.

Glooskap was the Big Man of the Micmacs, the Indians who lived in Nova Scotia before the white men came, and whose descendants you will find there today. The Great Spirit made Glooskap and gave him to the Micmacs to be their friend and teacher. He taught them the names of the stars and the trees and the flowers, where to find the biggest game and the finest fish, how to store food and cultivate their gardens. He was kind, he was good, he loved his people and would have died for them if he had been mortal as other men were.

Now Glooskap had an enemy, Guyadunsque the Beaver. When Glooskap brought the animals down from Skyland to live on the earth, the beaver was the last to be called, and he had borne a grudge against Glooskap ever since. He and his brother beavers were a great nuisance to Glooskap; they cut down his favourite birch trees, built dams where they did the most harm, and whispered gossip among the other animals.

Glooskap tried all sorts of plans to win Guyadunsque's friendship. He gave the whole of the Minas Basin to the beavers, so that they could make their homes and build a colony there; he fenced off a large grove of birch trees and gave orders that it should be kept for the beavers' use; he even told the Indians not to fish in the Basin, so that Guyadunsque and his friends should not be disturbed.

All this kindness did no good whatever. The beavers went on just as they had done before. They threw trees into the rivers where the people fished, dammed up the water so

28

that it flooded their gardens, and kept the whole Basin so untidy that Glooskap was ashamed to invite his friends to visit him.

Glooskap lived a very busy life. His people depended on him for everything; he settled their quarrels, gave them advice about their hunting, their games, and their families, doctored them when they were sick, made prayers to the Great Spirit when they had done wrong. The animals came to him too, and he taught their babies and bound up their wounds when they hurt themselves; moose, caribou, and many little wild things of the woods gathered round his wigwam, and he never sent them away until he had done what he could for them.

But there was one thing Glooskap never neglected, no matter how much work he had to do, and that was his garden. It was a very beautiful place, built in a curve of the shore at Advocate, opposite Blomidon, the great blue mountain where Glooskap had his wigwam. In this garden grew the brightest flowers, the tallest corn, and the finest roots and herbs in the country; for Glooskap was a wise medicine man, and there was no sickness he could not cure with his magic salves and potions. He did all the work himself, digging in the spring, sowing fine fresh seed, weeding and hoeing as the new plants came up, and harvesting his precious medicines in the fall of the year before the frost's sharp fingers nipped them.

Now, although Guyadunsque was an impudent fellow and clever enough in his own way, he never ventured to interfere with Glooskap's garden. Sometimes he and his friends piled wood chips and sawdust around the cove at Advocate, but Glooskap paid no attention, so the beavers got tired of doing it. One day, as Guyadunsque was swimming along past Advocate, he saw Glooskap working in his garden. Feeling more mischievous than usual, the Beaver pushed up to the shore and hailed the Big Man.

"What are you working at, Master?"

Glooskap stood up and peered out to see who was there. When he saw the Beaver's smooth brown head sticking out of the water, he smiled to himself; but he answered politely as he always did.

"I am weeding pumpkins, my son."

"Pumpkins?" said Guyadunsque scornfully. "Why don't you grow young birches or some nice red willow? Pumpkins have no taste at all."

"That's what you think," said the Big Man cheerfully. "Myself, I am fond of pumpkins."

He went back to his weeding, and as he stooped over it Guyadunsque noticed that he was wearing a fine necklace of purple stones. The beaver hitched himself up on the rocks so that he could see better. Certainly the Master had not worn these before, he thought to himself. I have never seen anything so beautiful. Presently he called out:

"Master, I have a sore foot. Can you give me some ointment for it?"

Glooskap knew the ways of animals well enough to suspect that the beaver was up to something; however, he always trusted people until they were proved deceitful, so he said:

"Come up here and I will look at your foot."

"It is very sore, Master. I am not sure I could walk on those sharp stones. Could you possibly bring me the lotion?"

Glooskap was surer than ever that the beaver had some trick in mind; but he went into the little wigwam where he kept his medicines and came out with a jar of salve.

"Let me see your foot," he said when he reached the shore. But Guyadunsque had slipped into the water again.

"I shouldn't think of troubling you, Master." He swam up and took the jar of ointment between his teeth, and as he stretched for it he had a good look at the purple beads—which was exactly what he had been planning for. They were even larger than he had thought, and they gleamed and shone like polished moonlight.

All the way back to his lodge the beaver muttered and grumbled to himself, as he often did when he had something on his mind.

"Purple beads! The size of gulls' eggs! *Were* they purple? They were the colour of the mountains when evening comes . . . the mountains! I wonder, I wonder?"

When Guyadunsque got home he called to him a young beaver who was known to be a bit of a gossip.

"Keeseegoo, you hear much. Do you know where the Master got his purple beads?"

The young beaver opened his eyes wide.

"Purple beads? The Master has no purple beads."

"You're no use to me," said Guyadunsque, and went out again. Sitting on a rock in the stream he called down Culloo, the great eagle.

"Culloo, you know everything. Do you know how the Master got his purple beads?"

But Culloo knew no more than Keeseegoo. He suggested that the beaver ask Blinker the Whale, whose work took him far out to sea and who was a particular friend of the Master's. So Guyadunsque went a whole day's journey to catch Blinker; but when he found the whale and asked his question, Blinker did not know.

"I can tell you how to find out, though," said the old fellow, puffing his great stone pipe that Glooskap had given him.

"Tell me, then," said Guyadunsque, "and I'll bring you a present next time I come."

Blinker wanted to know what the present would be, and Guyadunsque had to promise him a large catch of fish ("Goodness knows how I'll get them," thought the beaver) before he would say any more. When this was settled, Guyadunsque asked casually:

"What was it you said about the Master's beads?"

Blinker blew a neat fountain of bubbles, rolling his pipe round and round in his mouth.

"Didn't say anything about them."

Guyadunsque longed to give the whale a good smack with the flat of his tail; but remembering the beads, he held on to his temper and remarked amiably:

"You thought you knew someone who *would* know."

"No," said Blinker, whose slow speech and leisurely manner annoyed all energetic people. "Only said might tell you how to find out."

32

"Well, then," said the Beaver patiently, "how *can* I find out?"

It took a lot of prodding and questioning before Blinker said at last that if Guyadunsque would go to the point of Cap D'Or at the rise of the moon he might see something that would explain the purple beads. The beaver asked more questions, but Blinker simply turned his back and blew out a cascade of water that hit Guyadunsque square in the eye, so that for a minute he couldn't see an inch in front of him. When he had rubbed out the water and looked around him, Blinker was gone.

Guyadunsque swam home wondering whether Blinker had told him a story to get rid of him. However, he was really very curious about the beads; so that night when the big white star Fish-Hawk rose over Blomidon, the beaver went softly out of his lodge and paddled down the shore.

Just as he came around the cove below Cap D'Or, the moon pushed above the bluff like the upturned rim of a saucer. Everything was very quiet. The beaver, lying on a shelf of rock above the water, wished he had brought Keeseegoo with him. He did not go out much at night. The crooked shadows of the cliffs, the queer glimmer of moonlight on the water, and the dark towering outline of Blomidon looked strange; he felt he was in a new country. When a night-hawk screamed overhead, Guyadunsque almost fell off his ledge; the bird swooped down and spoke to him.

"What are you doing so late, little brother?"

In daylight Guyadunsque would not have bothered to

33

answer, for the beavers kept to themselves and had little truck with other creatures; but now even a bird was company.

"Just taking the air," he answered carelessly. "How fine the moonlight looks on the water!"

But the night-hawk had no time to admire the scenery.

"Good weather for moths," she remarked, and sailed off as fast as she had come.

The beaver's eyes were getting used to his surroundings; he gazed boldly out to sea, and was no longer disturbed by the moving shadows and the sharp black and silver outlines that looked so ordinary in daytime. Presently he thought he heard a faint sound, and stopped breathing for a second to listen. It came from across the water, a soft shush! shush! A canoe, thought Guyadunsque, who often watched the Indians going down to their deep-sea fishing. Now what Indian, said he to himself, can be out at this hour, and in my hunting-ground? He strained his eyes through the darkness and saw something moving towards him over the water. The gentle splashing drew nearer, and now the beaver lay very still, flattening himself against the rock, for he saw who was coming. The canoe was hollowed out of pure stone, white and unearthly in the moonlight, and at the paddle sat Glooskap, the Master of Blomidon.

The canoe beached at the foot of the bluff, and the Master got out and came towards the cove. Guyadunsque, blue in the face from holding his breath so long, dared not turn his head; but when Glooskap's footsteps had passed and the sound of them grew fainter, he moved a fraction of an inch and looked down into the cove.

The Master's back was turned, and he had something in his hand. Guyadunsque peered and scrabbled along the ledge. He could not see the thing, but presently he heard a sharp *clink!* as though two flints struck together. The Master moved forward a little, and now Guyadunsque saw clearly: he held a long double-pointed hammer, what we would call a pickaxe, and was using it to break into the rocky slope at the base of the cliff. Guyadunsque almost forgot that he was hiding, and stood up to get a better view. What *was* the Master at? First he used the axe briskly, with short strong strokes; then he stooped and lifted up a slab of rock that had come loose. The beaver's eyes popped: underneath the slab was quite a deep hole, and into this the Master dug his axe with long, swinging blows.

Standing on tip-toe, the beaver could just see the bottom of the pit, and suddenly he let out a squeak of excitement. Luckily for him the Master did not notice; he had stooped down and was picking little pieces of rock out of the hole. *Only they were not rocks, but big purple stones.*

The stars went marching over the sky and still Guyadunsque lay on the cliff and the Master quarried in the purple pit. The moon sank behind Cap D'Or, and Oaklahdahbun, the Morning Star, rose in her place; then Guyadunsque slipped softly into the water and swam away home.

Soon after this Glooskap went away visiting on the neighbouring island to the north, which we know as Prince Edward Island, but which the Indians called Epagweit, "Cradled-on-the-Wave". He left his wigwam in charge of his grandmother, who kept house for him, and his niece

Marten, who did the cleaning and cut wood for the fires. Before he went he warned them on no account to let anyone use his gardening tools.

"If you do," he said, "my enemies will get the better of me."

One night Marten and the old grandmother sat by the fire making moccasins for Glooskap. Marten sewed the skins together and the old lady worked patterns on them with porcupine quills dyed in bright colours. After a bit grandmother began to nod over her work, so Marten put her to bed. No sooner had the old lady dropped off to sleep than there came a soft scratching at the doorway of the wigwam. Marten went to see who was there, and found Keeseegoo outside.

"It's a fine warm night, Marten," said he. "Won't you come out for a walk?"

Now Glooskap was very strict with Marten, and would never have allowed her to go out at night, especially with one of the treacherous beavers; but it was stuffy in the wigwam, and the air outside smelt of dew and the wet bark of trees. Who would know, thought Marten, if she slipped out for a few minutes? She pulled the flap across the doorway of the wigwam, fastened it securely, and crept down the path beside Keeseegoo.

"What bright eyes you have, Marten!" said the young beaver. "They're like fireflies in the dark!"

Marten was pleased, because no one had ever paid her compliments before.

"And how fine your hair is, Marten! It is as smooth as

the tassels on the corn in the moon of the harvest. You are very beautiful, Marten!"

The foolish girl was flattered, and smiled and tossed her long black braids, for no one had ever said such grand things to her.

"Marten," said Keeseegoo as they went along, "would you like me to give you a present?"

Of course Marten was delighted, for no one ever gave her presents. She said: "Yes, Keeseegoo, I should like a present very much."

"Then you must get me the Master's long hammer," said Keeseegoo, "the one that has the two points, one sharp and one wedge-shaped. He won't mind if I borrow it."

But Marten said she couldn't possibly do that.

"We promised the Master not to touch the tools," she said, "and no one is to use them while he is gone."

"I can't bring you the present if you don't give me the hammer," said Keeseegoo, and he began to walk away from her.

Marten ran after him.

"Wait, Keeseegoo. If you promise not to tell anyone, I will get you the hammer."

"I will be more silent than the stones of the mountain," said Keeseegoo, "but get me the hammer quickly. If you want your present there's no time to waste."

Marten went down the mountain-side until she came to the little cave where Glooskap kept his gardening tools. It was hidden away between two great boulders, and unless you knew where to look you would never have found it.

The pickaxe was leaning by itself in a corner. Marten ran out with it quickly, afraid that someone might see her and tell the Master.

"Here it is," she said, thrusting it at the beaver, "but promise me you won't let anyone see it."

Keeseegoo promised, seized the pickaxe in his teeth, and hurried off.

Marten called after him:

"When will you bring it back?"

Keeseegoo answered without stopping:

"Tomorrow when Oaklahdahbun rises over Blomidon."

"I will be here," said Marten. "Be sure you're not late, otherwise Grandmother will wake up and I shall be scolded."

When Keeseegoo left Marten he went as fast as his feet would carry him to the beavers' lodge. Guyadunsque sat outside waiting for him.

"Here it is," panted Keeseegoo, throwing down the pickaxe, "and I hope you're going to get the stones. I had to promise the girl a present before she'd give me the hammer."

Guyadunsque took up the pickaxe.

"I shall get them. But you can't go throwing them round the countryside. They are to stay in our treasure-house until someone wants them badly enough to pay us handsomely for them."

"I must have one for the girl," said Keeseegoo, who could be stubborn when he chose.

"One then. But no more. Now go down to the foot of the bluff and watch; if you see anyone coming, whistle three times. And keep your mouth shut."

38

The next day as Marten went about her housework the old grandmother said to her:

"What have you got in your belt that shines so brightly, my grand-daughter?"

Marten replied:

"It is a new flower I picked on the mountain-side, Granny."

A little later the old woman said:

"What is that on your forehead that sparkles so gaily, my grand-daughter?"

And Marten replied:

"It is a bright pebble I found on the beach, Granny."

But Marten lied: for in her belt and on the band about her hair she wore the two purple stones Keeseegoo had brought her. Guyadunsque had given him one and he had stolen the other.

The next day Glooscap came home; and Marten hid her purple stones in a box and put it under the deerskin that covered her at night. The first thing the Master did was to visit his garden, and he stopped on the way for his tools. When he returned he said to Marten:

"Has anyone been in the tool-shed since I went away?"

Marten became very busy putting wood on the fire, but she answered promptly:

"Not that I know of, uncle."

"Someone has been in," said Glooskap. "My tools are not where I left them."

Now when Marten put the pickaxe back in the cave after Keeseegoo had returned it to her, she had quite forgotten which corner she had taken it from. She was frightened, for Glooskap loved to have things neat and kept each tool in its own place. However, she could not remember although she tried and tried; so she put it in the north-east corner, and murmured a prayer to the Great Spirit that it might be the right one. She forgot, as you and I often do, that the Great Spirit cannot mend people's broken promises; we have to patch them up ourselves as best we can and start all over again.

Glooskap said no more about the misplaced tools, and Marten hoped the danger was past. But the next morning there was trouble.

Marten heard of it from Culloo the Eagle.

"Do you know that the Master's beads have been stolen?" asked he, flapping down to sit on the centre pole of the wigwam.

"Beads?" said Marten. "What beads?"

"Ah," said Culloo, "ask Guyadunsque the Beaver. *He* knows."

Marten thought of the purple stones hidden in her box, and felt very unhappy.

"Who stole them?" she asked.

But Culloo only wagged his head and flew off, repeating, "Ask Guyadunsque."

By nightfall every man, bird, and beast on Blomidon knew that the Master's bead quarry at Cap D'Or had been broken into and that the beavers were responsible for it. Culloo the Eagle and Blinker the Whale told how Guyadunsque had asked them where the Master got his purple beads; and the night-hawk's story of seeing the beaver on the cliffs at moonrise made her popular at bird gatherings for many days.

The Master himself said little; but at nights Marten shivered under her deerskin, remembering his sad eyes looking at her. She had taken the purple stones down to the beavers' lodge and left them there, hoping that the Master would never know she had had them. But one day he said to her: "Why did you give away the purple stones, my daughter?"

Then, because he looked at her so kindly, Marten began to cry, and sobbed out the whole story, which was the best thing she could have done. Glooskap listened quietly until she had finished, and then he said:

"Flattery belongs to the powers of darkness, my daughter. They will steal the sparkle from your eyes and the smile from your lips, because those who listen to the Evil One cannot laugh. Keep the laws of the Great Spirit in your heart, so that you may be free and happy."

The rest of the tale is soon told. Glooskap set a trap below Blomidon for the beavers, for he felt they needed a lesson; but Keeseegoo hid in the bushes and saw what was done, and then ran to warn Guyadunsque. That night the beavers built a great dam of felled trees and broken bark across the Minas Basin from Blomidon to the Cumberland shore; and in the morning the waters overflowed and poured into the Master's garden. The corn was laid low, the pumpkins were washed into the sea, the neat rows of herbs and precious plants were torn up by the force of the water, and all the beautiful pebbles and shells that Glooskap had gathered to decorate his flower-beds went rolling down the cove and lay tumbled and broken along the shore.

Then Glooskap rose up in majesty and strode down to the sea shore. He took his great bow and broke the dam in pieces; some of them he hurled across the Basin to Advocate, where they lie to this day; but he dropped one piece where he stood, and it has been called Cape Split ever since. Glooskap's anger shook the rocks in the sea and swayed Blomidon like a leaf in the wind; thunderclouds roared in the sky, and jagged lightnings leaped upon the hills. All living creatures crept into their holes and dwelling-places, and for a night and a day no creature dared stir abroad. Then the Big Man's anger melted, as snow melts in the warm winds of spring; the sun shone, the skies became blue, the little animals went about their business, and life again took up its daily tasks. The beavers never repeated their evil trick. Moreover, they behaved themselves from that day forward, and if Guyadunsque still held his ancient grudge he kept quiet about it.

Sometimes amethysts are found in Glooskap's cove today; but if you get one and show it to an Indian he will ask you not to keep it.

"Put it back," he will say. "Those are Glooskap's beads, and when he comes he'll want them."

For the spirit of Glooskap still breathes on Blomidon, although the Master has long gone to the Happy Hunting

Grounds to make a home for his people. Perhaps you'll see him if you walk at moonrise on the rocks of Cap D'Or when Blomidon wears his purple robe at twilight and Fish-Hawk rises over the Cumberland hills.

How the Thunderbird Lost
His Courage

Once when Canada was young there lived on the top of
Mackay Mountain above Lake Superior the ferocious Thunderbird. You may have seen pictures of the Thunderbird,
or the big wooden images carved by the Indians and used
on their houses or their totem-poles; for they feared the
Thunderbird and yet respected him.

His nest was built among boulders and jagged crags on

the highest peak of the mountain. No Indian dared climb there, even if it had been possible, for when the Thunderbird was angry the mountain smoked like a mighty furnace, and tongues of forked fire shot from its sides. Here the young Thunders were hatched, and when they were fledged and left the nest their voices roared across the lake like a giant's kettle-drum, so that the black water heaved and foamed into great billows that went crashing among the rockbound islands as though a demon were driving them. Then the people in the valleys would shiver by their firesides and mutter to one another:

"The Thunders are flying again."

Now things had got so bad that the Thunderbird was almost master of the world. People were terrified of him and yet they admired him—a very bad state of things, for when you admire a person you try to do as he does. Very soon the chiefs began to swagger among their tribes as the Thunderbird swaggered across the sky. Because the Thunderbird flung redhot darts when he was angry and killed the folk who annoyed him, the chiefs took to beating their wives and lopping off the heads of braves who interfered with their wishes. Evil deeds spread through the land like a disease. Even the children caught it, quarrelling in their play and striking one another, and the villages became like battle-grounds, with every man set against his neighbour. Over all this turmoil flew the Thunderbird, beating his black wings and shooting lightnings from his eyes while animals fled to their holes and people to their houses

46

and even the rocks on the hillsides began rolling towards the valleys.

This sort of thing went on until the power of the Thunderbird became so great that he could move the whole human and animal kingdom as though they were one person. When he sat on Mackay Mountain and screamed, the people fell on their faces; when he arose and went hurtling through the sky, they rolled into their caves and wigwams; when he roared at them, "Come out!" they all crawled out and stood like wax figures with their faces turned upwards until they should be told to move again. Then the Thunderbird would shriek with laughter, flapping his wings and stamping his feet until the ground shook like jelly; and sometimes he would get out his fire-darts and shoot the people down in rows, *ping-ping, ping-ping-ping*, just to amuse himself.

At first the Indians prayed to Gitche Manitou, the Great Spirit, to help them in their distress. Then they grew so weak and brainless that they couldn't pray any more, and soon they forgot they had ever known Gitche Manitou, and went about like toys that move and jiggle when you wind them up. Because the animals were simpler-minded than human beings, they were not so easily led by the screamings and wind-flappings of the Thunderbird. They said to one another:

"He makes a great deal of noise, but underneath he is stupid. Many of us are cleverer than he is. Let us think very hard and perhaps we shall find a way to put him out of business."

47

So they sat quietly in their holes and thought, and the Thunderbird shrieked overhead, angry because the animals did not come out to be shot at.

Now there was one beast whose voice was seldom heard in the councils and gatherings; but when he did speak he always had something good to say and he said it boldly, fearless of what anyone might think. This was the Turtle, slow of foot and clumsy in his movements, but a steady creature and very determined once his mind was made up. While the animals discussed the Thunderbird, the Turtle as usual sat in his corner, keeping his neck in and saying nothing. Suddenly the Mink, who was conducting the meeting, turned to the Turtle and said:

"You're a smart fellow, Turtle. You hear a great deal and you see all that goes on. What do you think we should do?"

The Turtle jumped a little, for he was not used to being addressed so abruptly. He pushed his neck out and drew it in several times before he answered slowly:

"Think? I don't think at all, brother. I *know* what you should do."

The animals cried out together:

"Tell us, Turtle! Tell us what we should do!"

The Turtle answered:

"You should make the Thunderbird believe he is not as clever as he thinks he is."

At that everyone crowded round the Turtle, crying:

"How could we do that? Show us how to do that!"

The Turtle said:

48

"I have a plan. It may work and it may not; you'll have to let me try it."

Then he told the animals to watch carefully, but not to come out or show themselves.

"What are you going to do?" asked the Mink. "Can't we help you?"

"No," said the Turtle, "but stand by in case I have to come back in a hurry."

Then he marched slowly out to meet the Thunderbird.

It was a dark stormy morning. All night the winds and waters had trembled under the Thunderbird's fury, and now the great white sea-horses roared over Gitche Gumee, the Big Sea Water, tossing their foaming heads and drumming their hooves on the rocks; black clouds sat on the mountain tops and sent torrents of rain pouring down the crags and gulleys, so that between the lashing spray from the shore and the driving mist from the hills you couldn't see an inch in front of your nose.

Into this desolate scene the Turtle marched calmly. His feet went *squelch, squelch* in the mud, and the rain bounced on his shell like an army of tap-dancers; but he drew in his head and plodded on until he came to a little plateau surrounded by spruce trees, and here he found the Thunderbird. All around him were the skeletons of trees he had blasted with his thunderbolts; dead branches stuck out against the sky like huge scarecrows, and on one of them sat the Thunderbird, shaking his wings and saying fearful things under his breath.

49

When he saw the Turtle coming towards him he shouted with horrid laughter.

"Bolts and blazes!" roared he. "Is this the biggest man they could find for me to tackle? Look out for yourself, little insect!"

The Turtle looked at him, quite undisturbed.

"Shoot away," said he cheerfully. "I am come to let you kill me—if you can!"

Then the Thunderbird laughed so loud that people at Lake Nipigon, the other side of the mountains, heard him and ran into their lodges for shelter, and the Indians fishing from their canoes along the Kaministikwia River heard him, and said to one another:

"The Thunderbird is making a kill!"

And they drew in their lines and went home as fast as they could.

Meanwhile the Thunderbird had taken out his choicest arrows and was sharpening them with his beak. He was so sure of the Turtle that he did not hurry himself, and the Turtle for his part sat quite placidly under the tree, paying no attention to the insults being heaped on him by the Thunderbird.

At last the Bird got tired of sharpening arrows.

"Goodbye, insect," he shouted. "Say your prayers, earthworm! Your life is over!"

With that he spread his wings and hurled an arrow at the Turtle. Sparks flew from it as it hissed through the air. *Plunk!* it hit the Turtle squarely in the middle of his shell and *whing!* it bounced off the smooth polished top and fell harmlessly in the mud.

The Thunderbird looked down and was amazed to see the Turtle still sitting there unhurt.

"That was a very good start, old man," said the Turtle encouragingly. "Try again."

Then the Thunderbird shrieked with fury. Blue flame leaped from his eyes, and the dead trees clattered like castanets; with the fanning of his wings he loosed a shower of arrows, each tipped with a red-hot coal. *Bang, sizzle, plunk* they went, till all you could see of the Turtle was a whirling ring of fire.

"That'll finish him," snorted the Thunderbird. Then he heard a queer sound, like the fizz of a bonfire when you pour water on it; and he peered out sharply to see what it might be. All this time the rain had been pouring down, and great pools of water lay all over the ground. As fast as the arrows hit the Turtle's shell they bounced off and went *ker-plunk!* into the puddles. As their points touched the water they hissed and sputtered like angry geese, and clouds of black smoke soared upwards. It got down the Thunderbird's throat and into his eyes, so that he coughed and wept and couldn't see where to throw his darts.

"I say," said the Turtle anxiously, "you're not getting a cold, are you? Because if you are I think I'll go in. I catch cold very easily."

The Thunderbird stopped coughing and tried again to crack the Turtle's shell with his arrows; but the same thing happened, and this time the darts bounced so high that they came back and hit the Thunderbird under the chin. When this happened the Turtle laughed; and suddenly the Bird flew into one of his worst rages. He howled, he screamed,

51

he stamped his feet and tore his feathers. From Sault Ste Marie to the icy stretches of Hudson Bay the air was filled with flying pellets of fire. It was the worst storm anybody had ever seen in all that district. The young Thunders hurled themselves over the mountains; the sky went inky black and the seething waters of Gitche Gumee rose up to meet it; thunderbolts snapped off trees as though they were straws, and forked spears of lightning split huge rocks and sent them rolling like marbles down the ravine.

The Turtle drew in his head and flattened himself into the mud. When it was all over he peeped out. The Thunderbird was sitting on a stump, brushing his feathers and looking rather tired.

"I say," said the Turtle, "you're a bit done up, aren't you? You shouldn't work so hard, you know."

The Thunderbird didn't answer; so the Turtle went a little nearer.

"Do you know what I think?" said he chattily. "I think you're wasting your time trying to hit small creatures like me. You haven't been at it long enough. Why don't you try something easy—a nice big tree, for instance, or one of those islands out there? I shouldn't be surprised if you got quite good at it after a bit. It's amazing what practice does for one."

The Thunderbird looked down quite meekly and said in a small voice:

"Do you think so?"

"I do indeed," sad the Turtle. "You mustn't be discouraged right off like this. I'd suggest an hour a day

52

target practice—and while you're doing it I'll come and keep score for you."

"Thank you," said the Thunderbird, "but I think I'd rather be alone. I feel as though I'd like to rest for a little."

"By all means," cried the Turtle. "Thoughtless of me not to have realized that. I'll leave at once, and you can have a bit of a nap. Nothing like forty winks to put you right when you're down on your luck."

With that he turned around and started off for home at a pretty good pace, pulling his feet in and out of the mud with a soft *smack! smack! smack!* and chuckling to himself as he went. When he got to the other side of the clearing he looked back. The Thunderbird had gone down to the lake-shore and was standing there looking across to Isle Royale, the biggest island in Thunder Bay. Presently he stooped and picked up a pebble. Carelessly, as though for fun, he threw it towards the island. It fell short, hitting the water with a sharp thump. The Thunderbird picked up another pebble. Soon he was at it hammer and tongs, throwing stone after stone and getting more and more reckless as each one failed to hit the island. The whole matter was that the island was much farther away than it looked, and the Thunderbird was used to dropping things from above instead of shooting at them from the ground; but he was too much upset to remember this, and went on throwing stones all day, till by night he was so tired that he fell asleep on the beach and never went home to Mackay Mountain at all.

But the Turtle hurried back to the animals, who were

waiting for him in great anxiety; and when he told them what had happened they wanted to go at once to the lake and see for themselves.

"One at a time, then," said the Turtle, "but don't make a noise and don't let him see you. He wants to be alone."

So the animals crept down one by one, and there was the Thunderbird flinging stones like mad and muttering under his breath. The Turtle had carried the news to the Indians and they too came to see. One of them wanted to shoot at the Thunderbird with his bow and arrows; but the Turtle stopped him, saying:

"If we tried to kill him, it would be just as bad as when he was trying to kill us. Leave him alone; he's making his own punishment."

And the Turtle was right; for after that the Thunderbird never had time to chase and kill people, he was so busy trying to hit trees and islands. Once in a long while a man or an animal would be struck by one of his darts, but only if they were careless and put themselves in the way when he was practising. It must have been hard on the Bird, for he grew thin and most of his feathers dropped off; the heart was gone right out of him because he believed he could hit nothing smaller than a tree—and not often that unless he was feeling particularly strong and hopeful.

But it was a good thing for the people, for they were able to live in the open and grow their gardens and catch their fish for dinner without fear. Peace and goodwill settled over the land again, and the children sang at their play. But on Mackay Mountain the young Thunders grew

54

fat and lazy for lack of work and took to playing bowls on the mountain-top to while away the time.

On stormy days over Gitche Gumee you may hear the clap of the Thunderbird's wings and see the flash of his fire-tipped arrows; but unless you stand under a big tree you won't be in any danger, because the Bird is just getting in his daily target practice as the Turtle told him to do.

The Council-fire of the Five Nations

Have you ever walked or driven, or sailed in a boat, past the little town of Gananoque? Perhaps you have gone inland and followed the river that rises in a chain of blue lakes and wanders peacefully through pine woods until suddenly it comes upon a great pile of rocks lying in its path, and in a temper leaps over them and plunges down to join the Big River thirty feet below. The Indians, seeing this little river frothing and fuming on its way, called it Cad-a-nog-hue, "Rocks-in-Deep-Water", a word which our careless English tongues made into Gananoque. There are summer homes built above the grey rocks now, and their

57

smooth lawns reach down towards the shore-line where hundreds of years ago a great council-fire was lighted. So they say. I cannot swear that it happened here, or that it happened at all; but this is the story I heard.

Many, many years before the White Foot walked in Canada, two young men stood by the waterfall of Rocks-in-Deep-Water and looked out upon the Lake of a Thousand Islands. As you will see if you look at a map (if you don't like looking at maps you'll have to take my word for it), the Lake is really the Saint Lawrence River, which spreads along these shores in slow, lazy curves, carrying upon it the prettiest pattern of little green islands, for all the world like the decorations on a birthday cake.

Above the heads of the two young men rose the furry branches of pines and cedars; little brown cones fell *plop!* on their heads, but they paid no attention, for their faces were sad and they neither spoke nor looked at one another. They belonged to the Onondagas, one of the oldest clans of the Iroquois nation, and they were sad because their father, a great chief, had told them that unless they accomplished a certain task they could come no more to his wigwam and the village of their kinsmen. The task he had named seemed so impossible, and their efforts so small and weak, that one said to the other:

"See, it is hopeless. Our heads are dull, our hands as the hands of children; our father has banished us forever. Since we may no longer return to the games and the kinsfolk, the council-fires and the faces we know, it is better that we go to the Happy Hunting Grounds to await the coming of those we love."

58

So they had come to this high place above the river to wait for the hour of sundown, for it is then that the River God comes to carry departed souls to the Islands of the Blessed. The sun hung over the river, peering at himself in its coppery mirror; against the pale sky every tree on the little islands shook its ruffled head. The still bodies of the Onondagas looked like figures carved in bronze; unblinking they stared at the red ball of the sun, drooping nearer and nearer the water's brim.

Presently one spoke:

"Do you leap first, my brother, for perchance the River God will be angry if he sees two so young and ready to die. When you have made your peace with him I will follow, and surely he will not leave me alone in the darkness."

The other grunted, which might have meant Yes or No; and at that moment the lower rim of the sun dipped into the water. The boys stepped forward to the rock's edge, stood with arms raised and finger-tips touching, ready for the dive. The younger, who was to go first, was already poised tiptoe when the elder touched his arm crying:

"What is that beyond the sun?"

Through the golden haze of sunset came a solitary canoe, floating like a white feather on the gleaming surface of the lake. As it approached they saw an old man seated in it, his hair as white as the bark of the canoe. He gazed straight ahead, and his paddle fanned the water without breaking a ripple upon it. When he drew level with the rock on which the young men stood, he turned his craft and rode into a tiny cove of sand.

"He sees us," said one brother.

The other answered: "I am afraid."

And they drew back into the shadow of the pine trees.

The old man stood up in the canoe; he was of a great height, strong and majestic. He looked up to the two on the rock and waved his hand, beckoning. The Onondagas went down the narrow pathway, over tree-roots and through shrubbery, to the bottom of the ravine; neither spoke, for their hearts told them they must obey. They walked along until they came to the little cove and stood face to face with the boatman; and at once fear left them, for his face was as kind as the face of their own mother, and his eyes smiled.

"Greetings, sons of Koona," he said, and his voice was like the sound of the waterfall, deep and haunting.

The Onondagas bent their knees; but he bade them get up, saying: "I am no god that you should kneel before me." Then he made them sit down on the cool white sand, and himself sat beside them; and then he said:

"Sons of Koona your father, there is trouble in your hearts. Tell me your sorrow."

And because his eyes smiled and his face was as the face of their mother, the two young men told him all their grief, and how they had resolved to seek comfort in the Land of the Hereafter. The story was a long one, and hard to understand; so I will tell you quickly, lest you should weary of the stumbling speech of Koona's sons.

In those days the whole of this great land of Canada was inhabited by different races of men. In our careless

60

way we call them Indians, forgetting that their tribes and clans were as many as the stars of heaven, each one separate and different from its fellows. In the part of the country we are speaking of, there was a big nation whose name everyone knows—the fierce and splendid Iroquois, terror of the Hurons and very powerful. First, we suppose, they were all banded together in one kingdom. Then little groups broke away, moved to other places, took new names for themselves, so that after a time there were five nations instead of one, and the next thing was that they began to be greedy, and jealous of one another. They fought for the richest lands, and the rivers where the finest fish could be caught; they warred with one another and shed blood.

Among the elders there were some who mourned because of the angers of their tribesmen; and none mourned more deeply than Koona, Big Chief of the Onondagas. He would sit for hours outside his wigwam, smoking his great pipe and pondering ways to bring peace among the nations.

"We shall not always be an untroubled people," he would say to his sons. "There will be a time when great wars will descend upon us; we shall be overpowered and driven from our home. Where then shall be our strength if we are divided among ourselves?"

And he mourned yet more deeply, so that he grew thin and his coat hung limply upon him.

Then one day he called his elder sons to him and said:

"My sons, I have had a vision. In it the Spirit showed me that from you, sons of Koona, will come the freedom of our people. Go forth now, and return to me no more until you have accomplished all that my vision showed me. Walk to the uttermost parts of the morning, if need be, and challenge the black wings of night; but come not to the home of your kinsfolk nor darken the doors of my wigwam until this thing be done."

The sons of Koona made obeisance to their father, and they went away and hid themselves by the banks of the river Cad-a-nog-hue. We must ponder, they said, upon this work that our father has given us. But the more they pondered, the less they knew, and the longer they stayed by the river the more sure they were that the task was beyond the power of man. For, they said, the hearts of men are deep, as the deep river that runs over rocks, so that none may know what lies beneath. Who are we that we should command the nations to be at peace? And they were sad, and went forth to die at the place of rocks, as I have told you.

All this they spoke in burning words to the unknown man of the river, and he watched their faces and listened, and seemed to understand. When they had finished he said:

"It is a long road to the Land of the Blessed. Are you sure that you know the way?"

And they hung their heads and were ashamed. Then one said:

"Great Father, we were afraid. We did not know how to make the nations at peace with one another, as our father commanded us, and so we thought that we should die. A son that cannot obey his father is not worthy of life."

62

The old man looked upon them kindly. "If I should show you how to obey your father, will you then live?"

The faces of the sons of Koona became bright like the sun.

"Aye," they said together.

Then the old man rose and led them to the top of the highest rock along the shore, so that all that wide country lay stretched below them.

"Look," he said, and pointed to the south-west. "Across the river your tribes had their beginnings. First the Onondagas; from them branched the Mohawks, the Oneidas, the Senecas, the Cayugas. Each went to his own place, like leaves along a stem; each made his own laws, his own ways of living. This was well. But then discontent seized the tribes because they had not the Great Spirit in their hearts, and so they looked for other things. They wanted to own lands, they wanted to have better corn, larger fish, finer furs, grander villages, and more beautiful wives than their brothers; then, they thought, they would be happy because they would be strong and powerful and able to do as they liked. But it was not so.

"For the more the tribes struggled and fought with one another, the less happy they were; and although they had lands and food and houses and fine wives, their hearts were still empty, for the Great Spirit was not in them."

The old man ceased speaking and turned to the brothers, who stood very still waiting for what should come next. It was not what they expected.

63

"Sons of Koona," said the old man, "go gather fire-wood."

They looked at him amazed. He said again:

"Sons of Koona, go gather firewood."

They said: "But, master—"

Thunder rolled in the river-man's voice as he answered them, and lightning flashed from his eyes.

"When you drown and a branch is held to you, do you push it away? When you are lost and one points the way, do you refuse to follow?"

Trembling, they spoke no more, but went swiftly and did as the old man told them. From the woods they gathered firewood. They piled it high on the rocks by the river's edge: pine and beech and the red logs of the cedar, maple, and pale silver bark of birch trees. When the heap rose higher than their heads, the old man said:

"It is enough." Turning to the younger he said: "Build a fire."

So the younger brother stacked the wood and crossed it and laid on cones and small twigs; then with his flints he made fire, caught it in a handful of dry grass, and laid it to the edges of the brushwood. Round and round crept the little yellow flame, till the cones and twigs glowed red-hot; then with a joyous crackle it leaped through the crossed branches and waved a red banner towards the sky. The younger put on more wood; smoke streamed up, blue and yellow and rose-tinted, and floated in strange patterns across the river. The old man pointed to it.

"Sons of Koona, your message has gone forth. When

64

the tribes read the words you have painted on the sky, they will rise from their villages and wigwams, from their games and their hunting, and will gather about the Council-Fire to hear the words which you, sons of Koona who would die and now live, will speak to them. And from now until your father's commands have been obeyed, the flame of this fire shall not be put out nor its smoke cease to rise."

Then the two were afraid, and said:

"What words shall we speak who are young and know not what is in the hearts of men?"

But the river-man smiled and would not tell them.

"Keep the fire burning," he said, and walked away.

They were dismayed, and cried out: "Where are you going?"

But the river-man walked on; and when he got to his canoe he turned and waved to them.

"I shall return when you need me. Keep the fire burning."

And he pushed the canoe off as light as thistledown and vanished into the twilight.

All that night the brothers gathered wood and kept the great flames of the Council-Fire leaping into the darkness; and the smoke lay like golden mist between the river and the stars. When morning came they were weary, and the younger said to the elder:

"Do you lie down and I will keep the fire. When you have slept I will take my turn."

So they divided the day between them, working and

sleeping; but they ate no food, and at sundown they were faint, and staggered as they walked to and fro.

Then out of the shining west came the white canoe, and when the river-man stepped out he carried in his hands a basket made of reeds.

"Eat, sons of Koona," he said to the brothers; and he opened the basket and took out corn and meat, sweet honey, and a jar of spring water so clear that it ran like liquid silver when they poured it into their hands. While they ate, the old man tended the fire, and when they had finished he said:

"Sleep now and I will keep watch."

The brothers were too tired to ask questions. They made themselves a bed of pine-needles, and before the sun had left the river they were asleep.

Now the story of how the Five Nations met around the Council-Fire has been told in many ways by many people; but no one can tell you exactly what happened, because the Indians themselves never knew. Only the Onondagas who built the fire knew a little, and they did not tell. So we will have the story as it pleases us best, and if there is something you don't like you may change it to suit yourself.

From the land of lakes and rivers south of the Saint Lawrence came the tribes: the proud Mohawks, the Onondagas, silent and curious, the crafty Senecas, the Oneidas, the Cayugas. By canoe and on foot they came, painted and grim, their tomahawks sharpened and their arrows fresh-tipped with war points. Round the fire they sat, each tribe keeping to itself, each watchful and wary of the others.

66

From early morning till late evening they came, and all through the night; and there was food for them, and fresh water to drink. But when they asked: "Whence came the food?" none answered, for only the fire-tenders knew, and they spoke not.

When the eastern sky reddened with sunrise, the younger brother said to the elder:

"It is time."

Then the elder took into his hand the calumet, the Peace Pipe, and stepping into the firelight, pale now with the coming of day, he raised his right arm in salute and said:

"Brothers."

Every dark face in the circle lifted and the red dawn glimmered on the feathers, the ornaments, the war-paint, the flash of eyes watching the young Onondaga. About him as he spoke to them floated a golden light. Perhaps it was the sun shining through the mist from the river, but those who saw it bowed their heads.

Now the words that the Elder Brother spoke were never written down, and so we only know what happened afterwards. The chiefs who were there told the story to their children, and in turn it was told to their children's children, until at last it comes, beautiful as old things are beautiful, to you and me. Like a god he looked, they said, as he stood against the firelight with the Pipe of Peace in his hand and the golden light about his face; and the words that came from his mouth were golden too, like the music of melodies played on a reed. The hearts of the chiefs grew soft as they listened, and their fierce eyes became gentle as the eyes of young deer, for the voice of the Elder Brother was as the voice of their own thoughts, searching for the truth that every man desires.

When the Elder Brother had finished speaking, there was silence over that assembly, so that you might have heard a pebble fall into the river. Then the Elder Brother held up the Peace Pipe, bright with many-coloured feathers, and carved about the bowl with strange devices.

"Brothers!" he cried, and his voice rang out like a trumpet. "The Great Spirit has spoken. Let us throw down our weapons of war and smoke the Pipe of Peace. Let us make an end to our angers, our jealousies, and our quarrellings; for hate divides us, and while we fear one another we cannot become a great nation. I have spoken."

And he drew the axe from his belt and hurled it into the red heart of the Council-Fire.

Then with a mighty shout arose the chiefs and the sachems, their sons and their old men. Into the fire they cast their weapons, their clubs, and their tomahawks, their bows and sharp-tipped arrows; and the fire consumed them till nothing was left but a pile of stones.

Then the Elder Brother lighted the calumet, the Peace Pipe, and from hand to hand it went; and as the blue smoke curled upward, the Chiefs made a pact among themselves, that no more would tribe war against tribe and nation against nation, because the Great Spirit had come amongst them and peace was in their hearts.

While they spoke thus together and the hour drew near to sunset, there stood in their midst an old man who smoked

68

the Peace Pipe with them. They took him for one of the sachems; but when the brothers saw him they said to one another: "He is come as he promised."

Then the old man beckoned to them, and they came and stood outside the circle a little way off.

"Sons of Koona," he said, "you have done well. Because you were not ashamed to work with your hands, and to obey in the least things, the power of the Great Spirit came upon you and the people listened. Now peace comes to the nations, and henceforth they shall be as one; and the word of Koona your father has been obeyed."

He raised his arm and saluted them, and said:

"Sons of Koona, I go to my own place, and we shall not meet until we greet one another in the Land of the Hereafter."

The brothers said:

"Tell us your name, Great Father, that we may tell it to our children."

The old man smiled, and his face was as the face of the sun at noon-day.

"I have many names; and yet I have no name. Some day you will understand this. But when your children remember me, they may call me Hiawatha."

Then the brothers bent their knees and made obeisance; for in all the land no name was known and beloved so well as the name of Hiawatha, the Great Chief, who had lived none knew how long ago and whose memory was yet sacred to his peoples. No word could the young men speak for awe and wonder; and when they lifted their heads they

69

were alone. But far out on the river, floating like a white feather into the west, went the canoe of Hiawatha.

The two brothers went home to their father, and for aught I know they became great chieftains. I am sure that whatever they did was done wisely and well. The pact that was made round the Council-Fire became known throughout the country as the League of the Five Nations; and because their forefathers smoked the Pipe together and heard the voice of the Great Spirit, the tribes of the Iroquois live at peace with one another to this day.

The Legend of the Wishing Well

Through the heart of south-western Ontario there runs a little river named after the great river of England, the Thames. It is a friendly, comfortable little river. It does not leap across great rocks, like the mighty rivers of the east and west, nor rush down dangerous rapids, as its fiercer brothers do in lonely parts of the land; but like an old folk-song it sways and murmurs as it goes, and children bathe in it and lovers walk by it all through that pleasant countryside.

If you take the road that leads out of London and follows the river to the west, there is a certain spot where you may leave the highway and scramble down to the river, running cool and brown over pebbles and rocks; tall oaks and maples bend above it, and you'll have to slide between them as you go, for the banks here have a gentle slope. It will be worth the climb, for when you get there you will see in front of you the prettiest little waterfall, curling among the grey stones and making a delicate whipped foam in the bubbling current of the river. You may climb up to the top of the bank and see where the stream flows, clear as ice, out of the brown woods; you may kneel down, cup your hands and drink, and as you drink you wish.

Perhaps the Manitou of the stream will hear you and your wish will be granted; perhaps it is only an old Indian story. White folk call this waterfall the Wishing Well, but to the Indians it was the Holy Spout, whose waters could help a man to the Happy Hunting Grounds. This is how the tale began.

When the Munsees and the Delawares roamed the country, before the white people built towns and villages and brought their great steel railways roaring across the meadows, there lived near the banks of the river a beautiful maid named Winona. Her father was the chief of the Munsees, and a great man. Many young braves came to seek her hand in marriage, for the chief was rich and powerful, and besides the maid was fair and her voice bubbled and laughed like the voice of the river that ran below the village.

72

Among the braves Winona had two favourites: Wig-noed, her father's choice, and Ma-ga-na. Both were of the Delaware tribe, and both were young and handsome, but Ma-ga-na was the handsomer of the two. Wig-noed brought costly gifts for the princess, ornaments and gay clothing, arrows tipped with the finest flints; Ma-ga-na was poor, and brought only flowers freshly gathered at sunrise, and baskets woven from sweet grasses and reeds. Winona was just as kind to one as to the other; she smiled at both, accepted their presents, walked with them at the river's brim when the sun lay low on the western slopes.

But the two young men were bitter enemies. Each hated the other; each tried to outdo the other. If Ma-ga-na could not bring beautiful gifts to the princess, he was better able to amuse her than his rival: he was the fastest runner, the strongest wrestler, and the best player at snake-stick of the whole tribe. On the other hand, Wig-noed was the better hunter; Ma-ga-na was too kind, and sometimes let a deer escape him because he admired its soft bright eyes and graceful body. Wig-noed thought this faint-hearted and womanish, and used to mock Ma-ga-na when the braves were out hunting.

"Yah, chicken-heart! Where's the buck I saw you trailing? Put on a skirt and go home to your grandmother, baby-face!"

But Winona never said a word. She praised Wig-noed's skill with the bow and accepted the skins he brought her; but she welcomed Ma-ga-na just as sweetly, and put his nuts or berries beside Wig-noed's deerskins. Often the braves would beg the princess to set them some task in which they might compete for her favour. But she never would, because she couldn't bear to set one against another.

"I like you all equally," she would say. But that did not satisfy the braves, and they were suspicious of one another, saying: "You walked longer with her than I," or "She honoured my present more than she did yours."

At last the chief her father said to Winona:

"This cannot go on. You must choose between your suitors, otherwise there will be war in the village. My young men are at one another's throats already. Give them a contest of skill and let the winner be your bridegroom."

Winona did not dare oppose her father; but in the days to come she was very sad. All the village was in a state of excitement over the contest, which was to take place at the Moon of Strawberries, the fairest time of the summer. Everyone knew that the prize was to be the hand of the Princess Winona, and many a head wagged over a camp-fire as the old women said to one another:

"Ah-ha! Now she will have to choose!"

That year the summer was the finest ever remembered, even by the oldest squaws nodding in their wigwam doorways. Never were skies bluer, suns more golden; dog-roses bloomed like stars in the meadows, and over woodland clearings the wild strawberries lay in cool clusters among their pointed leaves. For three days the young men of the surrounding villages ran, wrestled, hunted, and competed in all manner of games; for three nights the Moon of the Strawberries hung its lantern of pale gold above the river.

Throned among roses sat the Princess Winona. As each contestant came panting from the field, the onlookers shouted and applauded, but never by speech nor action did the princess show her opinion of the performers.

The last day of the contest arrived, and excitement was great among the crowd, for the swiftest and most cunning of the braves had been kept till the end, and among them were Wig-noed and Ma-ga-na. No one doubted that the princess's choice would be one of these two. But which one? Nobody knew, but everyone was guessing. Little boys were doing a lively trade taking bets on the winners, and the old squaws chuckled among themselves.

"Ah-ha!" they said. "Now we shall see where her heart is!"

But the Princess Winona neither smiled nor sighed, and her cheeks were as pale as the moonlight on the river.

That day the feats accomplished were more brilliant than ever. The spectators were hoarse with shouting, the children ran and danced in the field of combat. On a bench beside the Princess Winona stood a stone bowl filled with the juice of crushed strawberries; this was to be given to the winner as a token of victory. The princess was dressed in her most beautiful robes of white doeskin; her mantle, girdle, and moccasins were embroidered in as many colours as there are in the sunset, and she wore scarlet wood lilies in her hair. Around her the young maids who were her attendants babbled and ran to and fro, but she sat as moveless as the silver birch whose branches spread above her.

At last every man had tried his luck except the two

young braves, Wig-noed and Ma-ga-na. The watchers drew a little closer towards the field, and a shiver of excitement went from one to another. All eyes turned for a moment to the Princess Winona, sitting alone and silent beneath the birch tree; but she neither looked nor uttered sound.

Through the list of accomplishments went the young men. They ran, they leaped, they shot, they struggled for mastery in games of skill; but the crowd for all its breathless watching could not make judgement between them. Ma-ga-na outstripped Wig-noed at the races: his arrow reached the farthest mark, his craft with the hoops and javelins was matchless. But when they were ordered to go out and hunt trophies for the princess, Wig-noed brought back a buck's head and two young does, while Ma-ga-na could only show one little rabbit-skin.

Thus when everything was finished and the two stood panting and wiping the perspiration from their faces, the eagerness of the people could not be held back.

"Proclaim the winner!" they shouted. "Make known the leader of our young men that we may celebrate the victory!"

But the princess sat like a stone in a lonely pasture, deaf to the tumult surging about her. The chief her father came to her and whispered in her ear:

"Rouse yourself, girl! The sports are over, the people await your choice. Would you shame me by this dreaming?"

Then Winona opened her eyes and looked upon the crowd before her, and upon the young men waiting with

76

heaving breasts and anxious eyes. Wig-noed stood proudly, his unbound hair flying in the wind; but Ma-ga-na looked down upon the ground as though he listened and feared.

Slowly the princess arose, and with one graceful movement she took the stone bowl in her hands and faced the people. Silence fell upon all that assembly, as though a voice had called them. Towards the princess they strained their eyes, and the young men were paler than the stem of the birch tree.

"People of the Delawares and of the Munsees, my friends and my kinsfolk." Clear as falling water came Winona's voice upon the air. "Since you have placed this choice upon me, not by my own free will but in accord with your wishes I do this thing." She paused, and a stir as of the wings of birds passed through the listeners. Winona continued:

"These sports and games that we have seen have given you pleasure. I, too, have taken delight in them. To set one performer above another is surely as useless as to praise the song of a bird and then to shoot it with arrows; but because it is your will, I do it. This bowl," she raised it in her hands, and the eyes of the multitude followed it, "is to be the token before you of the one whose skill I deem the greatest."

She stopped speaking, so that even the winds held their breath and were still. Then she said (and her words were like arrows tipped with fire):

"By the Hands of the Great Spirit who made me, I swear

that my judgement is true and right. I proclaim the braves Wig-noed and Ma-ga-na, of equal skill and mastery, to be the winners of this tournament."

Then, while all who heard it gasped for amazement, the Princess Winona beckoned to the two young men, Wig-noed and Ma-ga-na. To her they came—Wig-noed pale and angry but Ma-ga-na with great joy—and knelt at her feet. Stooping, she held the great bowl to their mouths, and they drank together until it was empty. The Princess flung the bowl to the ground and broke it into a thousand pieces.

"So breaks all strife between you forever," she said, and gave a hand to each of them, raising them to their feet.

Then the people shouted and danced, in praise of Wig-noed and Ma-ga-na and of the cleverness of the Princess Winona. But the Chief shook his head and would not join in the rejoicings.

"It is an evil thing that she has done," he said, "and evil will come of it."

Now the old chief's words were wise, and it happened as he had foretold. Instead of their differences being forgotten, the jealousy between the two braves grew more and more bitter, so that they spoke no more to one another and their hands crept to their tomahawks as they passed each other on the trails. Moreover, Winona was seen more often with Ma-ga-na than with Wig-noed. She said no word to her father, but the old man watched her as she went from the wigwam in the hours of twilight, and his face wrinkled into deep lines of anxiety.

One evening when the air was warm and still, and bats

cheeped lazily as they swung among the low branches of the cedar trees, Ma-ga-na walked on a high bank beside the river where it ran clattering and murmuring over a rocky ravine; and beside him, quiet as a moth's wing, walked Winona. Their faces were happy in the moonlight, and although they did not talk, they seemed to understand one another. Wild creatures of the woods passed them and birds going to roost chattered over their heads, but they heard and saw only each other. Thus they did not know that Wig-noed stood behind a clump of oak trees and watched them as they walked; they did not see his eyes burning in the dusk nor the moon-rays glinting on the thin blade of his tomahawk.

"Maid of the Munsees!" Ma-ga-na spoke softly, but the watcher behind the oak trees heard. "The moonlight upon the face of the water is not so fair as thy face. Twilight is in thy hair and the scent of roses. Truly, thou art beautiful!"

Then Winona answered (and her voice was as the murmur of wood-pigeons at nesting-time): "Swift are thy feet as the west wind. Tall thou art as the young birches beyond my father's wigwam; thy hands are strong and very merciful. The deer in the forests do not fear thee, nor the small furred creatures who run among the flowers in my garden. Because of these things my heart is warm for thee, Ma-ga-na of the Delawares!"

And Ma-ga-na laughed for joy, and the two walked on very lovingly. But behind the oak trees Wig-noed shook with the might of his anger, and he swore a great oath as he stood in the path of the twain who came onward.

Past the clustered oaks they came, happy with each other, looking not to right nor left, and as they passed they saw not the shadow of Wig-noed as he bent to his tomahawk.

"I love thee, Rose of all the world!"

They stopped in a circle of moonlight. Tree shadows danced on their faces, and as they kissed the forest held its breath. Then a cloud blotted the moon, and in the darkness Winona screamed.

Red were the fallen leaves where Ma-ga-na lay; but as the moonlight shone again he lifted himself and with his dying strength plucked out the tomahawk from his breast and whirled it above his head. It smote Wig-noed as he turned, and he fell beside the body of Ma-ga-na whom he had slain.

Alone in the moon's circle stood Winona, her doeskin mantle stained with blood, and she held the tomahawk in her hand.

"Ma-ga-na, my lost lover! I come! I come!"

All the village heard the cry, and they came in haste, following the voice of Winona. They found her there, on the crest of the river-bank, and beside her the two braves; in death their faces were gentle, and their hands touched as they lay, as though in the Land of the Hereafter they loved one another.

But where the princess died there sprang a stream of bubbling water that danced down to the river and fell laughing over a rock; and the sound of it was the voice of Winona, as in life she had laughed and sung. So they called the stream the Holy Spout, and those who washed in it were sure to go to the Happy Land whither their princess had gone before them, where huckleberries grow as blue as summer skies and good Indians live without sorrow forever.

On moonlight nights beside the Wishing Well you may kneel to dip a cup of water, and perhaps through the woods you'll hear a voice that mingles with the waterfall.

"Ma-ga-na, my lost lover! I come! I come!"

The Woman Who Was Tired

If you should sail a boat up the north coast of Labrador until you come to the great gateways of Nakvik Bay, you will notice on one of the tooth-edged points a strange-looking stone. At first you might take it for another of the misshapen rocks that rear like witch-faces from the shore; but as you approach you will see that it has the form of a woman, sitting with her chin in her hand gazing out to sea. If you pull your boat in close, you might see a little heap of food or tobacco on her stone knees, or even a necklace of bright beads hung round her neck. For the natives love her and bring her presents.

Any Eskimo living in this part of Labrador can tell you her story. This is how it goes.

Once upon a time (and that always means a long while ago) there was a village. It straggled along the shoreline of Nakvik Bay, and all round it rose the fierce jaws of the Torngats, the "Devil Mountains". A dark, haunted place it was, the water as black as the towering rocks; and the spirits of the people were dark too, as though evil shadowed them.

In the village lived one girl who was different from the rest. Her name was Mikak, and she was all alone. Her father and mother died when she was little; she had no brothers or sisters, and she was very beautiful. Her hair was softer and finer than that of the village people, her eyes larger and brighter, and her skin was as smooth as ice under water. She was clever, too; the clothes she made for herself were better shaped and better sewn than the other women's, and so they were jealous and sharp-tongued, whispering among themselves when they saw her going out in her caribou coat and fur hood.

"She thinks too much of herself," they said. "Because she has clever fingers she makes us look plain and dowdy. After all, who is she to hold her head so high? We'll teach her a lesson!"

And they caught Mikak and took her pretty clothes away, and told her she was to be their servant. Mikak was too gentle to stand up for herself. She was afraid of being put out of the village and left to starve; so she did whatever she was told—which was the worst thing she could have done. For the more obedient she was, the more she was given to do. She worked from morning till night, and did all the hardest and dirtiest jobs, so that her smooth hands grew knotted and horny, her back bent like a willow twig, and her face in the fur hood grew thinner and thinner until it could scarcely be seen at all.

Although she was so pretty, Mikak had no young brave to take her walking at night when the moon shone coldly over the Torngats. Some of the village boys would have liked to ask her, for she was bright and gay and understood their fishing and hunting stories much better than the other girls did; but they were afraid of their mothers, and of being laughed at by the rest of their friends.

So Mikak sat alone while the boys and girls went fishing along the shore, or scrambled among the rocks for bunch-berries and wild poppies; and in winter when the families gathered in the huts, she had to stay in the corner where it was cold because no one would let her sit beside them.

One day there came to the village a party of Indians, Montagnais from the inlands, on their way home after a fishing journey to the south. They put up their tents along the shore, and some of the Inuits (which is the rightful name for the Eskimos) went down to barter furs and hear the news of the world.

Among the travellers was a young Indian who had made his first trip southward. He was full of interest and enthusiasm, and came among the villagers to see how people lived in these strange parts. It chanced that the first person he saw was Mikak; she was carrying firewood from the shore to keep the cook-fires alight. He took the heavy logs from her and carried them himself, a thing that none of the village lads would have dreamed of doing.

"You must not carry those," he said to her quite crossly, "they are too heavy. Where is your husband or your brothers? Let them help you."

Mikak looked at him and said nothing. She was not used to being spoken to except in harsh words, and she was embarrassed by the handsome stranger. But he repeated his questions. At last Mikak said:

"I have no brother nor husband."

"Sisters then," said the Indian. "You must have sisters. Where are they?"

Mikak said: "I have no one but myself."

Then the young Indian put down the wood and looked at Mikak fiercely.

"That is not good," he said, and Mikak put up her arm quickly, for she thought he was going to strike her. He took her by the arm.

"Come with me," he said, and his voice was gentle. "We will walk in the woods, and as we go we will talk."

Now there were no woods in that wild place; but up the mountain sides and in the small plateaus between the ridges there was scrub of bear-berry, creeping birch, and black spruce. Here Mikak and the Indian walked. It was August, the Moon of Flight, and as they went they looked for bunch-berries, and Mikak gathered the flaming fireweed and held it in her arms. The Indian showed her how to

86

bind the flowers into her hair. They laughed together, and Mikak forgot her fear and weariness.

But when she got back to the camp she was beaten for being so long away.

The Montagnais stayed for several days in the village. Every day at dawn Mikak and the young man walked on the mountains, and every night at moonrise they sat on the shore and watched the light break over the Torngats. On the last night the Indian said:

"Mikak, tomorrow at dawn we break camp. By nightfall we shall be far away. It is not right that the great mountains should stand between thee and me; our hearts will be torn with sorrow and our lives will be without joy. Come with me and we will say to the mountains, 'Be opened' and to the rivers, 'We fear thee not', for they will part us no longer."

And Mikak looked at the Indian's face, his broad shoulders, and strong hands; and she wept because she was happy.

The moon was full that night, and every pebble on the shore glittered like gold. The Indian and the Inuit maid walked against the lighted sky. Each saw only the other's face, heard only the other's voice, and they did not look behind them. They did not see a black shadow moving from rock to rock; did not hear a stone slip, a dry leaf rustle, nor feel sharp eyes upon them as their hands touched in the moonlight.

Next morning while the frost-fumes of night still hung above the bay, the Indian encampment packed its tents and moved away. Long after the rest of the party had started, a lone figure lingered on the shore, straining its eyes towards the village. It was the young Indian, waiting for Mikak. But no one came. All the huts were silent and closed, like houses of the dead. He came nearer, called her name; but there was no sound except the drowsy cheeping of birds and a cold wind blowing in the tree-tops.

At last the Indian went back to the shore, sick at heart. As he sat there one of his brothers came running.

"What are you doing sitting here while we carry the pack-loads? Come away. There are devils in this place. I smell them."

So the young Indian went away, and he heard not the voice of Mikak calling to him:

"Come back! Come back, my love!"

For Mikak's enemies had listened while she spoke with her Indian lover in the moonlight; and they had told the old woman that she was going to run away. Then the women rose up and said:

"She runs away, does she? Leaves us to do all the work! Ah-ha! We will see about that!"

And they took Mikak while she slept, and tied her hand and foot so that she could not move. Then they put her into a deep cave in the mountain-side and fastened her to a rock.

"Cry to your Indian lover!" they mocked her. "Call aloud; doubtless he will hear thee!"

But the walls of the cave were of solid stone, and when Mikak lifted her voice it was like a little mouse crying in the darkness, so that she wept and was silent.

88

After that things went from bad to worse for Mikak. She worked harder than ever; when her day's labour of fire-keeping, wood-cutting, water-drawing, and all manner of drudgery was done, the women would set her to work making new clothes for them or mending their old ones. Her own garments hung upon her in rags, for she was so thin that they no longer fitted her, and she was not allowed to have new ones. Soon she scarcely cared what she did or how she looked; day and night were alike to her.

"I am so tired, so tired!" she would say over and over again, but no one listened to her.

Years went by. Mikak was no longer a young girl and her strength began to fail. Often she could not finish her work, and would fall exhausted while she was carrying wood or tending the fires. Then the young women, the strong ones, would beat her and cry:

"Up, grandma! Don't be so lazy! Don't you know we must be warmed and fed? Get on with your work!"

This kind of thing could not go on forever, and at last Mikak fell sick. She tried to get up as usual, but her limbs would not obey her, and she fell on the ground faint and ill.

"Look at her," said the young women. "She is useless. Throw her out of the village!"

The other women took up the cry. Several of the older men tried to interfere, pitying the sick woman; but they were shouted down and pushed out of the way. The young men and girls seized Mikak, carried her to the outskirts of the village and flung her on the rocks, shouting:

"Call on your gods to help you, lazy one!"

Mikak was so weak that she slipped off the rocks and rolled into the water. She did not know how long she lay there, half in the water and half out; but the cold waves lapping on her face and head revived her, and presently she was able to drag herself to the rocks again where the sun warmed and dried her.

Sitting there, resting her head on her hand, she watched the gulls wheeling overhead and wondered bitterly why she had not died.

"I wish that I *were* dead," she thought. Then she looked up at the blue, brilliant sky and felt the fresh wind in her hair, and she thought:

"It is quiet here by the water, and everything is good and beautiful. If the Great Spirit takes care of these wild birds, perhaps he will take care of me also. How nice to be one of these rocks, always sitting in the sun, able to be quiet and rest all day long. That is what I should like."

Now as she was saying these things to herself, one of the gulls flew over her head and began to circle round her. The Inuits say that when a bird flies three times round your head, whatever you are thinking will come true. Whether that is so, or whether the Great Spirit heard Mikak's words, I do not know; but the fact remains that as the gull made his third circle round her head Mikak felt herself being gradually turned to stone. It did not hurt. Her body fell into a comfortable, easy position, her chin rested in her hand, and all the tiredness and sorrow and bitterness crumbled away from her, leaving her quiet and peaceful.

90

Night passed over her, another day began, and Mikak in her stone body rested beside the water. All the fair things that she had missed in life, scents and sounds and colours, the brushing of birds' wings and the delicate breath of flowers, came crowding to her now, and she took them in and thought about them.

"I should have trusted the Great Spirit before," she thought. "How stupid of me to have wasted so much time. There must be something I can do to make up for it."

Mikak had all time before her, and so she did not hurry herself. She went on watching and listening and taking things in until by and by the thoughts she had began to glow and sparkle, so that her body reflected them as sunlight reflects in a mirror, spreading warmth and colour over the cold stone. People going past began to notice her, saying:

"Look at that rock! It seems as though it were alive!"

And they came again to see if their imagination had tricked them.

After a time they named her "The Thinking Image" because she sat so calmly with her chin in her hand looking out to sea. They liked to look at her, and more and more people came. Children loved her—they sat on her stone knees and patted her hair and cheeks; soon they brought presents for her, things to eat and drink, pretty trinkets, and bits of jewellery. The old men brought tobacco, and the women lifted their babies up for her to see. She who all her life had been unhappy and deserted now was loved by all.

And who shall say that the spirit of her Indian lover, long ago gone to the Happy Hunting Ground, did not return and sit there with her in the sun?

Stay awhile in her quiet presence; it will do you good. And when you leave at last and turn to wave farewell, you will see that she is smiling.

The Great Peace

Once upon a time in the Lands of the Sunset on the west coast of Canada there lived two tribes. The first tribe lived on the southern part of the coast where the Capilano Canyon lies between the shoulders of the mountains; the second tribe lived among the fjords and islands of the northern coast; and beside and beyond them both spread the blue Pacific Ocean. Both tribes sent their brown chil-

93

dren to wade on the beaches and catch crabs and starfish in the rock pools; both fished the rivers for salmon and picked fruit along the valleys; and both made prayers and feasts to the Great Spirit at seedtime and harvest, because to him they owed the breath that warmed their bodies and the earth that gave them sustenance.

So it was a pity that these two peoples, who might have been good neighbours, hated and made war upon each other. The north tribe wanted the whole coast to hunt in and the south tribe would not let them have it; and so they fought bitterly and killed one another, and the land was dark with anger.

Now in the south tribe there was a chief who had twin daughters. They were beautiful girls who had never known fear or hatred. In the deep valleys of the Capilano they grew up, and at the knees of the mountains they learned their prayers so that they talked easily to the Great Spirit and heard his voice among the high snows.

Perhaps it was because of their goodness that the Chief their father decided to make a great feast when the time came for them to put aside their childhood and become grown women, able to take on the responsibilities of homes. It was the custom to do this for young women; but the Chief wanted to make this feast more notable than any other because of his daughters' gentleness of spirit.

The war, he felt, could look after itself for a few days; he was winning it in any case, and even if his enemies should gather their strength while he feasted he could easily overthrow them again. So he called in his war canoes and bade the people prepare food and fine clothing for the big potlatch he would give for his daughters.

Meanwhile the twin girls sat in their lodge that faced the sea, watching the tide roll in and roll out; and their faces were sad.

"It is good that our father stops the war in our honour," they said. "But when the feast is over and the war canoes go again to the battle, what then? Will not our hearts be weary and our womanhood wasted before the fruits of this bitter strife be ready to taste?"

And they rose from their couches and went hand in hand to their father.

When he saw them coming, tall as the young poplar trees and lovely as dawn on the mountains, he greeted them and said:

"Full of grace are you, my daughters!"

They bowed before him and answered:

"Our heads are bent before thee, our father, as the grasses before the face of the west wind. We would ask a favour of thee, our father."

The Chief lifted them and seated them before him.

"Say on, my daughters."

The taller of the girls, she whose face was bright and clear as the full moon, spoke thus:

"Our father, we are glad because of the great feast you make in our honour. Our feet are ready to dance and our lips to sing; but there is one thing that grieves us. In the country beyond us live our cousins of the north; we would have them also to feast and share our merriment."

The Chief was amazed, and he said:

"We are at war with these people, my daughter. You cannot feast with your enemies!"

But the twins cast their eyes downward and were silent. Then the Chief was perplexed, and he said:

"Will nothing else content you, my daughters?"

And they answered: "Nothing."

The smaller twin, she whose eyes were kind as the eyes of young deer, touched the hand of the Chief her father and she whispered to him:

"Do as we ask, our father."

And because the Chief loved his daughters and believed in their goodness, he did the thing they desired, although nothing like it had ever been known in the land. On every headland of the coast friendly fires were lighted. Into the enemy waters went the war canoes of the southern Chief, but instead of war cries and weapons of death they carried an invitation to attend the feast of the twin daughters.

Then the people of the north put by their war-paint and their weapons. They took their wives and their children, their best possessions and their stores of food, and they got into their painted canoes and came with songs and laughter to the sea-ways of the south where the water ran red with blood only a few suns before. Along the warm sands the children of the two tribes played together, happy with new companions; the women from the north brought their fish and game to the camp fires, and over the roasting meat they exchanged stories with the women of the south until they were as merry as squirrels in a nut-tree.

From time immemorial no feast had equalled the one that now began. There was food in vast abundance, for the visitors had brought gifts of fish and meat as well as many things beautiful and curious—necklaces made of coloured stone, shapely baskets of woven cedar bark and of twined roots of the spruce, wonderful fabrics of dyed goat's hair, clubs of carved whale-bone in strange designs—these they laid at the feet of the twin daughters. There were games and contests while the sun moved across the sky, and at night under the moon, singing voices kept time to the soft shuffle of feet that danced.

For many days it went on; as long as there was food by day and music by night nobody bothered about going home. But at last the fires died out, and one morning in the cool grey mist of dawn the long, sharp-prowed canoes of the northern tribe drew up along the shore, and the people went into them. The tribe of the south stood watching, and as the canoes nosed out into the smooth silver water they who sat in them waved their hands and cried:

"Farewell, O brothers!"

And from the shore the people answered:

"Farewell! Farewell, O hunters of the north!"

Into the mist of morning went the canoes, and the pale hands of dawn received them; silent upon the shore stood the watchers, their faces strained northwards. The rays of the sun came over the sea, and the canoes were swallowed up in it; and the young men said:

"They are gone. The feast is over."

Then the Chief turned to the young men and said:

"Call out the canoes. We go a-fishing."

The young men asked: "What of the war, O father?"

The Chief looked upon them, upon their strength and beauty, and he smiled.

"You dream, my children. There is no war. Call out the canoes, for we go a-fishing."

So peace came to the Lands of the Sunset, and there was war no more because the twin sisters who talked to the Great Spirit had learned that people who laugh together do not hate one another.

Now it seemed a pity that these sisters should grow old and men should forget the good they had done, so the Great Spirit took them in the beauty of their youth and set them high on the mountains above the Capilano Canyon. He dressed them in pearl-coloured mist and set white crowns upon their heads, and there they sit to this day, twin peaks above the great city of Vancouver, their shining faces lifted to the sky, giving thanks to Gitche Manitou for the blessing of peace.

The Coming of the White Men

Now as the Gitche Manitou walked in the garden, he saw that certain things needed doing. There was a great deal of waste space; there were too many trees, and the people were not very good at cultivating the soil.

"I had better send someone to help them," said the Gitche Manitou. "They need a few fresh ideas."

So he picked up one or two men from another part of the world and set them down in the garden.

The newness of everything went to their heads a little, and instead of being a help to the brown men of the garden, the pale-faced strangers pushed them out of the way, and took charge themselves.

"It is a pity," said the Gitche Manitou, watching, "but they will have to learn. Some day the brown and the white will share the garden together."

But that day was a long way off.

The Legend of the Sleeping Giant

You who love the tales of long ago brought to us by murmuring voices round a camp-fire, by old men whose grandmothers whispered in their ears at bedtime, by songs crooned over birch-bark cradles—hear the story of Nanna Bijou, the Giant of the Ojibways.

Nanna Bijou lived with his grandmother near the Falls of Niagara. No one remembered his parents; Nokomis, his grandmother, said that he was sent from the sky to save his people.

"What shall I save them from, Grandmother?" Nanna Bijou used to ask when he was a little boy. But Nokomis did not know.

So he grew up big and strong, taller than the tallest of the braves, cleverer than all his playmates. He knew where the birds had their nests and where the timid hare hid her babies; he called the animals Brothers, and the birds his little children. The Indians respected and looked up to him, for the cornstalks in his garden grew ten times as many ears as other people's cornstalks, and he could make beautiful white maple sugar by drawing sap from the trees and setting it to dry in the sun, whereas everyone else had to boil their syrup in great kettles before it would harden.

Life was pleasant along the Niagara River; food was plentiful. Nanna Bijou cured those who fell sick, and Gitche Manitou smiled upon his people. So it was strange that in spite of all this Nanna Bijou was not happy. He lost his habit of laughing and grew quiet and silent; he went for long walks by himself and would be away for days at a time. His grandmother noticed it first, and she said to him:

"Are you sick, my grandson?"

But Nanna Bijou said that he was not sick. The next day his grandmother asked again:

"Are you in love, my grandson?"

But Nanna Bijou said that he was not in love. Nokomis could think of nothing else that made young men sad; so like a wise woman she said no more.

Nanna Bijou grew sadder and sadder, and presently the Indians noticed it, and they said:

102

"What ails you, Nanna Bijou?"

But Nanna Bijou did not answer them; and they wondered among themselves and were troubled.

One day an old chief who was a friend of Nanna Bijou's found him sitting on a log by a little stream, looking into the water, and the tears fell from his eyes and ran into the creek so that it wept as it moved over the pebbles. The old chief sat down beside him.

"Why do you weep, my son? We have seen that your heart is heavy; share the burden with me, that I may lighten it."

Then Nanna Bijou lifted his head and answered:

"My heart is heavy, O wise one, because I have dreamed a dream."

The old chief said: "Tell me your dream."

So Nanna Bijou told it. He had seen a white canoe coming up the great river from the east; it was larger than any canoe he had seen before, and it had wings like a bird. Because of the wings it moved fast, and in it were strange men.

"They had white skins, white as the wings that moved the canoe. And there was pale hair on their faces and on their heads; it fell to their shoulders like the brown tassels of the corn. I could not tell what they said to one another, but I knew that it was evil. Then I woke, and it was dark, as though a cloud hid the sun; and I was afraid. Many times I have dreamed; always the faces are clearer and the voices louder. Soon I shall know what they say, and then it will be the end."

103

A few days later the old chief came by the lodge where Nanna Bijou and Nokomis lived. Nanna Bijou was outside, putting a new handle on an axehead. He looked sad no longer, and he was singing to himself. The old chief stopped.

"What is it that you are singing, my son?"

Nanna Bijou sang:

> *I am bringing new songs,*
> *New songs to a new land.*

The Chief said: "You are happy, my son."

Nanna Bijou laid down the axehead and came to where the Chief stood.

"Listen, O wise one. The dream that I told you came again. Last night I heard the words of the strangers, and now I know what I must do. So my heart is light, for it is what a man does not know that troubles him. That is why I sing a new song, O wise one."

The Chief asked: "What are you going to do, my son?"

And Nanna Bijou answered:

"I go to the far north, to a land where the white stranger comes not. I call my children to follow me, for as surely as they stay here they will be driven forth to die. The wings of the white canoe bring sorrow to my people and desolation to my brothers of the woods and waters; therefore I go, and they who are wise will follow me."

Then Nanna Bijou took his new axe and his bow and arrows, and Nokomis brought her possessions tied in a bundle. They took a day's food with them, and Nanna Bijou bade farewell to his people.

"Where I go you shall come also," he promised them, "only have courage, and follow. In the new lands we will make peace for ourselves, in the new country we will build our homes; there we shall not be troubled, and our children shall grow up in safety."

Nanna Bijou walked away, and Nokomis with him, and the people went to their homes and began to gather up their belongings—all but a few, and they said:

"What a pack of old women you are, to be frightened by the dreams of a madman! Nanna Bijou has an evil spirit; if you follow him you will die in the wilderness. We will stay in our homes; no harm can come to us there."

So they stayed; and the white men came and drove them out, and took their homes and their lands and their possessions. They fled into the forests, seeking the way that Nanna Bijou had gone, but they could not find it, and they perished or were taken prisoner.

But they who had obeyed Nanna Bijou were saved.

Nanna Bijou and his grandmother walked for many moons. They travelled round the rims of the Great Lakes; they followed vast rivers; they camped in the forests, living on the fish they caught and the wild roots and berries they found. They walked and walked, and many adventures befell them, so many that if I told you all the stories they would take half a lifetime to read.

At last they came to a wild country of black rocks, balsam forests, and ragged tumbling rivers rolling around a mighty stretch of water. On the top of the highest mountain sat the Thunderbird, whom all the Ojibways feared and whom none had ever seen. When the Bird saw Nanna

Bijou and Nokomis, he began to scream and flap his wings, and Nokomis cried out in fear. But Nanna Bijou went up to the foot of the mountain and shouted:

"Come down, O Thunderbird!"

And while Nokomis hid her face for fear, the Thunderbird alighted on Nanna Bijou's shoulder; he rubbed his beak on the giant's hair, and Nanna Bijou stroked his feathers.

"Don't be frightened, Grandmother," said Nanna Bijou. "This is our home from henceforth, and the Thunderbird is our friend and counsellor."

And so it was. Nanna Bijou made his home on an island beside the lake, which he named Gitche Gumee, the Big Sea Water; the bay where the island stood was called Thunder Bay, and he appointed the four winds, Wabin, Kabin, Kabikowk, and Shadwana to guard the bay and keep out strangers and evil spirits. They let in the Indians who followed Nanna Bijou from Niagara, and then the bay was locked with a great double-headed key, which was kept in the nest of the Thunderbird.

Now there was a secret about the island where Nanna Bijou lived, and it was known to no one save the giant, his grandmother, and a few of his closest friends. The secret was that the whole island was built of solid silver, with a thin coating of rock and soil over the top. Nanna Bijou had seven great shovels made, and he and his friends quarried the silver and stored it in caves underground.

It happened that an Indian of the Sioux tribe, visiting the Ojibway settlement, overheard some of Nanna Bijou's friends talking, and so learned the secret of the Shuniah, the hidden silver. The Sioux, whose name was Atatharho, thought to himself:

"If I could get hold of that silver I should become the mightiest man on the earth."

For Atatharho did not know very much, and he thought that the Big Sea Water and the land surrounding it were the whole world. He lay awake night after night planning how to get the silver for himself. By listening at doors and hiding behind trees and bushes, he discovered that the key to the bay was kept in the Thunderbird's nest.

"I must get that key," he said to himself, "then I shall be able to unlock the bay and let my people in, and they will destroy Nanna Bijou and take the island."

But getting the key was no easy matter, for the Thunderbird sat on it all night and the Four Winds guarded it by day.

"I must think of something," said Atatharho; and he thought and thought, till his head ached and his brain was dizzy. One day he heard Nanna Bijou and two of his Indians talking.

"Never let the word 'Shuniah' pass your lips," Nanna Bijou said to them. "If a pale-face should learn our secret, it would mean death to all the tribe."

Atatharho crept away laughing to himself. The Pale Faces! Why hadn't he thought of them? The Great White People, whom even Nanna Bijou feared, whom even the Thunderbird obeyed! He got into his canoe and paddled swiftly across the Big Sea Water until he reached Sault Sainte

Marie. Here he went on foot, and before long he met some white men hunting in the woods. Atatharho made friends with them, and around their camp-fire he drew pictures for them on a piece of birch-bark. He showed them the Big Sea Water; he drew the rocks and the bay, and then he drew Nanna Bijou's island and in their ears he whispered "Shuniah". The white men knew that word. They asked Atatharho many questions. How could they reach the island? Where was the Shuniah to be found?

Atatharho took his birch-bark and drew the Thunder-bird with lightnings coming out of his mouth and Nanna Bijou on legs as tall as pine trees, and he showed it to the white men. But they laughed and said that they were not afraid of birds or giants.

A few days later, as Nanna Bijou sat on his island looking across Gitche Gumee, he saw a white canoe coming towards him. It skimmed the blue water as lightly as the swooping wings of a gull, and in it were men who sang in a strange tongue.

Nanna Bijou went into his house.

"Make fast the doors," he said to Nokomis. "Stay inside, and whatever happens don't come out until the sun shines again."

Then he called the Thunderbird and said:

"Tell the people to take all their possessions into the caves below the mountain, and to stay there until the sun shines again. Then they are to come out and go northward, to the hills and the lakes and the plains. There they shall make their home, and they shall not return to the land of

Gitche Gumee, for it is theirs no longer. Nanna Bijou speaks."

When Nanna Bijou had done these things, he bade farewell to his grandmother and went alone to the high mountain above the bay; and there he talked with the Great Spirit.

"O Mighty One, who sees all things! I have done as you commanded. I have brought my people to this place and they have flourished. Now the enemy has come, and my time has come also. I have done what I could, and you must do the rest, O Gitche Manitou!"

Then Nanna Bijou bowed his head and went down from the mountain. And Gitche Manitou made a great storm. He took the waters of the lake and tossed them up to the sky; he bent the mountains like a bow across his knees, and wrapped the land in a shroud of snow. The Ojibways stayed in their caves, as Nanna Bijou had told them to do. They heard the rain and the hail and the rushing cyclones above them, but they were not afraid, for they trusted Nanna Bijou.

At last there was quiet, and one of the Indians peeped out to see what was happening. He saw blue sky over his head, and heard birds singing; the sun shone, and the snow had melted away. The people came out of the caves and they saw that everything was changed. The little silver island had disappeared, and in its place rose a great pillar of rock. On it, with his face to the sky, lay the giant Nanna Bijou. He looked happy there, and peaceful, sleeping his long sleep. The people left him food and weapons so that when he woke up he would know that he was not forgotten; for they knew that Nanna Bijou would never lead them again. They were not sad, for, they said, his spirit is sleeping, and when he wakes he will go to the Land of the Hereafter to make a place for us. We shall meet him there, beyond the river of shadows, when we have paddled our last canoes homeward.

And the people of Nanna Bijou went northward, and they made a home there as Nanna Bijou had said; and there their children live to this day.

But the gates of the Big Sea Water have been unlocked to the world ever since, for the Thunderbird left the double-headed key lying at the entrance, and there you may see it in the shape of two great canals. The white men who came to steal the silver perished in the storm, and Atatharho with them; and the secret of the Shuniah was never known, because over the island lies the stone body of Nanna Bijou, the Sleeping Giant. You will see him when you look across the bay from Port Arthur. He lies on Thunder Cape, his face turned to the sky, waiting for Gitche Manitou to wake him up.

The Birch Trees of Temiskamingue

Once upon a time in the beautiful lake region of northern Quebec there lived two birch trees. They were very much in love with one another, which was sad because between them stretched nearly ten miles of deep, sparkling water. It was a lake which the Algonquin Indians who lived there called Te-mis-ka-mingue, which means "deep water". The two trees they called Koo-no-ha-ha, meaning "She who dwells by rushing waters", and Chi-Chi-koue, "He who rattles the leaves". Koonohaha lived on the east shore and Chichikoue lived on the west, and between them the River Ottawa rolled its mighty current into the lake and out again.

You would wonder how these lovers could talk to each other across so many miles of water; or how they came to fall in love at all. It is simple enough really, for trees have better eyesight than we have; on clear days the birches could see one another quite well, and Chichikoue would nod to Koonohaha, and Koonohaha would nod shyly back. They soon arranged quite a good telegraph system; for instance, two nods meant, "Good morning, how are you today?" and three nods meant, "I am quite well, thank you. How are you?" One nod was "Yes", and a little shake of the branches meant "No", while three nods and a shake meant "I love you. I wish you were here beside me." This last one was done so often that the Indians noticed it and thought that the Manitou, or Spirit of the Lake, used the trees for his messengers, so they protected them and never allowed their branches to be cut or their bark torn off.

Now these trees had first noticed one another when they were very young saplings. By the time they were half grown they were sending messages to each other by the East and West Winds, who very kindly ran a postal service for them across the lake. They were simple people, not asking much of life; they ran their roots deep into the earth and drew up the food and drink they needed, and they liked all weathers—the hot sun of summer, the fresh winds of autumn that took off their dusty leaves and left them clean and tidy for winter, the gentle tap of snow on their branches, and the warm life-giving rain of spring that stirred the sap in their veins and dressed them in their new green clothes.

But amidst this pleasant life they had one great wish. They thought about it all day and dreamed of it all night; they wanted it so much that day by day the sun seemed less warm and the moon less bright because they could not have their heart's desire. This was to grow side by side with each other, to be able to talk to one another in tree language—that soft, tinkling sound you hear when you walk in the woods.

But the birches did not know how to make their dream come true. All the other trees in the forest stood happily in the places they had grown in, for years and years and years, till they grew old and their trunks cracked; then a wind-storm came along and pushed them over and they died. How could they be so contented, the birches wondered? Had they never looked across a stretch of shining water and seen the one person in all the world they wanted to live beside?

One day Koonohaha spoke about it to the great pine tree who lived next door.

"Don't you ever get tired of standing there?" she asked. "Don't you wish you could live somewhere else—across the lake perhaps?"

The tall pine looked down at the little silver birch and smiled through all his dark branches.

113

"My little lady," said he in his big booming voice, "when you are as old as I am you'll know that wishing never brought anybody anything. I have done a great deal of thinking in my time, and I have decided that if the Great Manitou put me here, this is where He probably needs me most. I presume He knows what He's about; it would be childish for me to make a fuss."

The pine tree dropped a brown cone into the water and watched it float away, then added thoughtfully:

"Of course, I do not know everything. I *have* heard—long ago—that one may win the heart's desire if one suffers enough. There may be ways and means. . . . But I am not in love, you see. It makes all the difference."

Now as it happened the pine tree was right; being in love did make all the difference to these two, and eventually their wish came true, though not quite in the way they had imagined, which often happens when we want something very badly. This is how it came about.

On the western side of Lake Te-mis-ka-mingue (that is, on the side where Chichikoue lived) there was an Indian encampment. These Indians were Algonquins—tall, strong, straight-limbed men who shot, hunted, and fished in the surrounding woods and lakes, tilled their gardens, married handsome wives, and were a busy and peaceful tribe of people. They had their regular feasts and customs, and one of these took place every month at the full moon. When the hour of midnight was come they would assemble on the lake-shore, the chiefs and their wives and their children, the young men and the old men, pretty brown girls with long braided hair, little papooses strapped on their mothers' backs; they would build a big bonfire and offer sacrifices of meat to the Manitou of the lake.

Every month since they were tall enough to look over the scrub of juniper and blueberry that grew round their feet, the birch trees had watched this Feast of the Full Moon; they loved the sharp tang of the wood-smoke curling up through their branches, the smell of burning pine needles, and the tawny bodies of the Indians dancing in the moonlight. The lake would be full of strange colours, the tom-toms would beat out monotonous music; above the forest would be heard the long lonely cry of a loon far out on the crystal waters.

When the sacrifice had been offered and the fire burnt low, there would come a great silence, and all the Indians would sit motionless upon the rocks, waiting. Even the birches held their breath, afraid to let so much as a leaf tremble for fear of disturbing the spell.

Then down the rippling pathway of the moon would come a wonderful sight: a long, pale canoe, transparent as the wings of a moth, its paddles moving without sound, and in it ghostly figures, sitting straight and still, their hollow eyes gazing towards the western shore where the waiting Indians sat. Inch by inch they drew nearer, until the prow of the canoe almost touched the outermost rock of the shoreline; then the phantom paddles would be still, and the white faces of those who sat in the canoe could be plainly seen. Cries of joy and wonder would come from the Algonquins as one by one they recognized relatives and

115

friends; for these were the spirits of departed warriors of the tribe who came monthly at the full moon to visit the living and to look upon the faces of their loved ones. Never a word they spoke, although the living cried out to them; they sat without movement, pale and sombre, and only their eyes moved and seemed to speak what their voices could not utter.

Then as silently as they came they would vanish; the paddles would move, the canoe turn about, and cleaving the golden water as faintly as an insect's wing it would disappear on the rim of the eastern shore. Koonohaha watching them go out and return, never saw where they came from nor whence they vanished.

Now it chanced that one day, near to the full of the moon, Koonohaha was looking down at herself in the mirror of the lake and thinking how pretty she was. There was nothing conceited about it; she took pleasure in her beauty because it made her more worthy of Chichikoue's love. Presently she heard the distant swish of paddles and looked up expecting to see some of her Indian friends coming across the lake to fish. Instead she saw a fleet of strange canoes and in them queer-looking people. As they came closer she saw that they wore a great many clothes of peculiar shapes and colours, and tall headdresses with feathers curled around them. But the most frightening things about them were their faces: they were pale, like the waxen flesh of snowberries, and on their upper lips were thin patches of hair with long ends that turned upwards.

Koonohaha knew nothing about history nor the discovery of America or she would have seen at once that these were white men, and that the peaceful days of the Te-mis-ka-mingues were nearly over. For this was the seventeenth century, and the canoes belonged to a Frenchman named De Troyes who was exploring the Ottawa with his *voyageurs*. The little birch tree did not know any of these things, and she wished that her tall strong Chichikoue was beside her to protect her in case the white strangers should be enemies.

The canoes were heading for the east shore; soon they drew in almost at Koonohaha's feet. She could see them clearly, and heard them speaking a language she did not understand. They landed their boats and came up into the woods, making a lot of noise and breaking the bushes with their rough boots; night was falling and they wanted a place to camp. Presently the leader of the party gave an order.

"Cut down some young trees and build a shelter. There will be fish in the lake and we can get food enough to last us several days."

One of the men came crashing through the undergrowth. He carried a short strong axe and he stopped beneath Koonohaha.

"Here's a good one," he shouted to his mates. He swung his axe, and the little tree felt a shuddering blow through all her delicate branches. She cried aloud to Chichikoue, but he could neither see nor hear her, for dusk was drawn like a curtain over the lake.

It did not take long for the white man's axe to cut

117

through the slender trunk of the birch tree; with a last despairing cry she sank to the ground and lay helpless on the rocks with her pretty head dipping into the water. The men wasted no time admiring her; they stripped off her branches and went to look for more trees. By the time they had cut all they needed it was too dark to build the shelter, so they rolled themselves in their cloaks and went to sleep near their boats.

Koonohaha lay very still; the rocks were damp and cold, and every fibre of her body ached, but she was wide awake, and as she listened to the snores of the white men an idea came to her. "If I could get into the water," she thought, "I might be able to swim across the lake." She was so bruised and wounded that every movement hurt her; but she found that by making an effort she could roll a little from side to side. Each roll brought her a little nearer the edge of the rock; it was slow work, and very painful, but at last her courage was rewarded. One tremendous effort . . . she was over, the cool water bubbled round her, and as she rose again to the surface she lost consciousness.

Meanwhile, on the western shore the Indians had watched the arrival of the white men. Piskaret, wise old chief of the tribe, summoned his council and said to them:

"War chiefs, shamans, warriors all, that which has been foretold has come to pass. Our lands have been invaded, our peace is ended; for these are the conquerors, the men of the pale faces, come across the seas to destroy our nation. Nevermore will our dead return to us at full of the moon, never shall we behold them until we join them in the Land

118

of the Setting Sun; for the White Man's Curse has fallen, and the Spirits of the Red Men vanish forever from the forests and the rivers, the lakes and the mountains. Behold, we are a race forgotten until our children and our children's children shall have learned the ways of the conquerors."

He finished speaking, and all who sat about the council-fire bowed their heads. Then a young Indian leaped up and cried:

"We have been deceived! The Manitou of the Lake promised that this should be our home forever. Now his word has been broken. He is an evil manitou, and we will obey him no longer, for the White Man's Curse has come upon us!"

Then the Indians cried out loudly against the manitou; they chanted war-cries and danced about the council-fire.

"It is the full of the moon!" they cried. "We shall see whether our fathers will come to visit us!"

Slowly the yellow ridge of the moon crept over the eastern sky; the light rose like a banner and flooded the waters of the lake. But no pale canoe came floating with ghostly riders; empty lay the moon-swept waters, and the Indians sat silently round their dying council-fire. Then the young chief sprang to his feet and pointed upwards.

"This tree was the messenger of the Manitou. He spoke evil words, he brought vain promises. He shall die!"

And with his axe he struck a ringing blow at Chichi-koue so that he quivered in all his branches.

"Down with the evil messenger!" shouted the Indians, and they cut him to the ground and flung him into the lake. "Take back your messenger, O Manitou!"

Koonohaha pushed her head above the water. For a second she wondered why she was having this terrible nightmare; then she remembered. The rocks . . . the white men . . . the cruel sting of the axe . . . the cold shock of the water closing over her. . . . Of course; she was on her way to Chichikoue; she must be half way across the lake now. She could not lift her head to see the shore, but she saw the clear cool orb of the moon above her, and she knew it must be long past midnight. She wondered if she was going in the right direction. She tried to move her stiff limbs, to swim as she had seen the fish doing; but she had no fins to flap as they had, and the water pushed against her and rolled her over so that she could not see where she was going.

"Oh dear," she thought, "I shall never get to the other side at this rate. Perhaps I am going the wrong way; perhaps I shall never see him again. How unlucky I am!" And she added her tears to the cold water of the lake, and felt very unhappy indeed.

Now when Chichikoue was thrown into the water by the Indians he had only one thought in his mind.

"I shall float out on the current and then swim to the other side," he said to himself; for being a man he naturally knew more about such things than Koonohaha.

So the current floated him out to the middle of the lake

as he had expected; but instead of swimming—which wasn't as easy as he had thought—he found that he was being carried swiftly down the stream, far from the shore he wanted to reach. He fought with all his might, but the great current of the Ottawa, flowing through the lake, was too strong for him, and he was swept along as though he had been a blade of grass.

"Alas," he thought, "I shall never see my lady again; we shall be parted forever. How unlucky I am!"

At that instant he felt a gentle bump against his side. It must be a big fish, he thought; perhaps he can tell me how to get to the other side of the lake. The bump came again, and a frightened voice said:

"Oh dear me, whatever can that be?"

What a beautiful voice, though Chichikoue, and he poked his head above water to see whose it might be. At the same instant Koonohaha poked *her* head up; and so these two saw one another face to face. Very different it was from the meeting they dreamed of; but they knew one another instantly, and cried out together:

"Oh, *where* have you been? How did you get here?"

Side by side they floated under the moon, and told one another all that had happened. They talked so long and so busily that they had left the lake far behind before they noticed it, and were sailing down the broad waters of the Ottawa, on and on, past hills and valleys, on and on, through calm lakes and angry rapids; day followed night, and night again followed day, and still they travelled and talked. And at last they came into the wide blue stretches of the Lake of Two Mountains, by the trading-post of Mount Royal, and there the fur-traders saw them and pulled them out of the water and laid them to dry in the sun. Then, because they were sturdy trees, rounded and smooth and fine, the traders took them up and built them into the new lodge they were making, laid them one on another and bound them firmly; and so at last their hearts' desire came true, and they were parted no more, until the house crumbled into dust and the spirits of the trees went together to the Land Beyond the Setting Sun.

Still at Lake Te-mis-ka-mingue the moon rises red as an orange behind the eastern shore; but never again came the spirit warriors to look for their descendants. Perhaps the ghosts of the Algonquins still haunt the rocks of Te-mis-ka-mingue when the moon is full; I do not know. Some day I shall go and see.

Qu'Appelle

Once upon a time, before the white men planted wheat upon the plains of Saskatchewan, a young brave came from the south and travelled by lake, river, and portage to the dwellings of the Crees, along the chain of waters near our city of Regina. Only there was no city then, nothing but the green valleys that followed the river-courses, the brush woodlands that grew about the valleys, and the lakes strung like blue beads between the hills. And round and beyond the hills and the water-ways lay the prairies, farther than eye could see, rolling in gentle curves beneath the dry western sun.

Now the young Indian, whom we will call Morning Star (because his real name has never been told), was making a journey that had become familiar to him. Many years before, when he was a small lad, he had wandered with his father in the north country of Canada, and a friendly tribe had given them food and shelter. Here beside a beautiful river Morning Star met a little girl whose happy face and laughing eyes made him think of the bright flowers he had found on the prairies. He called her the Little One, the Prairie Rose. He played with her, and made a tiny canoe out of birchbark for her to sail on the river.

Every year when the heat of summer was past and the first crisp winds of autumn reddened the maple leaves, Morning Star came with his father to the land of the Crees, and every year he found the Little One, the Prairie Rose, waiting beside the river. Time slipped by; the children grew up without knowing it. Each year they measured one another against a big poplar tree that grew on the river bank, and each year the notches they cut mounted higher. There came a time when Morning Star stood against the stem of the poplar tree, and as the Little One tiptoed to mark the notch above his head she cried in wonder:

"How tall you are grown, O Morning Star!"

Morning Star stepped aside and looked at the place she had marked, and with his knife he cut the notch deep and true. Then the Little One stood against the tree and he marked a notch for her, and lo! it was a head's length below his own.

"Last year you stood as high as my heart," said Morning Star, "and now you are at my shoulder. How tall you are grown, O Prairie Rose!"

And they looked at one another, and behold, they were children no longer, but a grown man and woman. Tall and strong was Morning Star, with broad shoulders and black, tossing hair; very lovely was the Little One, slender and light as a birch sapling. Both of them were brown, brown as winter leaves, and their faces shone with laughter.

That year when it was time for Morning Star to leave his Cree friends he called the Little One to walk by the side of the river where they always met and where they had played as children. The face of the Little One was sad, and as they walked she sighed and said:

"My heart is heavy, O Morning Star."

Morning Star took her hand in his and said:

"Rose of the Prairie, my heart is heavy also, for I must go to the land of my fathers, and when I leave thee the sun loses his brightness and the songs of the birds are stilled. Yet I have joy through my sadness. Look." He pointed to the west, red with the setting sun. "The light of our day is sinking. Soon he will be gone and darkness comes. Yet turn and look to the east; tomorrow those tree-tops will be flooded with the white light of dawn. So will our happiness return, when the year comes again to the harvest and the trees are hung with gold. Then I shall say to my canoe,

'Northward, northward', and ere the swallows wing to the south we shall be together again."

The sun slipped below the river and the air blew coldly upon them; they bade one another farewell, and said Morning Star:

"When I come again, O Prairie Rose, we shall be married and go together to the land of my fathers. Never again shall I take the trail alone from the land of the Crees!"

And the Little One nodded and smiled; but her heart was heavy because there was darkness on the river and no moon lighted the sky.

That was a long cold winter on the prairies. The snow was so deep and the ice lay so long on the river that food grew scarce, and when spring came at last the people were weak and sickness broke out in the villages. The Little One's mother died, and many of her friends and relatives; always she went among them, fearless and tireless, soothing the sick and comforting the dying with her whispered words of courage.

But sometimes she was very tired, and when she lay down at night she could not sleep for weariness; then she would creep from her lodge and go through the dark, scented woods until she came to the notched poplar tree by the river. Here she would sit listening to the water. The sound of it soothed her, and she would dip her fingers in its coolness and whisper to it:

"Come soon! Come soon, O Morning Star!"

And the river carried the whisper, mile on mile, along lakes and tiny streams, past green valleys and desolate plains,

126

and it soared into the air and hung among the tree-tops, so that the birds heard it and called to one another:

"Come soon! Come soon, O Morning Star!"

Far away in the south Morning Star prepared for his journey to the north country. All the summer he worked at his canoe, rebuilding it and strengthening it and making it beautiful inside and out. With pine-tar he smeared it, and with resin he bound the seams; on its bows he made a pattern of porcupine quills, stained with the bright juice of roots and berries, and the form of the pattern was a prairie rose.

The moons of summer crept past, the slow heat of July and the sharp dry stillness of August. One night as Morning Star came home he felt the nip of frost on his cheek and saw the golden leaves dropping, one by one, upon the roof of his tepee. Then his heart leaped as the salmon leap in the river, and he cried out in joy:

"I come, O Prairie Rose!"

Next morning, as the blue mist of early fires floated among the trees, Morning Star launched his canoe and headed northward. He was very happy, and as he paddled he sang an old French song that he had learned when he was little from the *voyageurs* who went up and down the rivers of his native country. They had taught him their language, and as he grew up he spoke it more easily than his own.

The days of the warm Indian summer passed swiftly as Morning Star's canoe threaded its way among the waterways of Saskatchewan. He was close to his journey's end;

127

another portage, another stretch of closely wooded river and lake, and he would be out on the shining river that flowed straight to the home of the Little One. Morning Star's heart leaped again for joy, and as he paddled he sang:

> *C'était un vieux sauvage,*
> *Tout noir, tout barbouilla,*
> *Ouich'ka!*

The sun was touching the tree-tops to the west as the canoe nosed its way into a narrow passage between thickets of birch and willow. Down to the river's edge they marched, making deep shadows on the water; lily-pads clung like clutching fingers to the prow of the canoe, and the long hairy stems of water-weeds pulled at the paddle. Morning Star shivered under his deerskin jacket; the place was gloomy, and suddenly he was afraid. There was no sound except the push of his paddle against the choking weeds; then a hawk cried harshly overhead, and again the cold chill crept about him. He tried to sing, but his voice echoed dismally in the silence, so he gave it up and paddled as fast as he could. Darkness came on; a faint cold wind blew in his ears.

All at once he heard someone call his name. He listened, startled. The voice came again, clear and strong.

"Morning Star!"

He stopped the canoe and peered into the woods; there was nothing to be seen, no sound to be heard. Morning Star leaned on his paddle, his heart beating fast. Had he dreamed, he wondered—fallen asleep as he rowed? He listened again; the wind lifted the hair on his forehead, and then came the spirit voice, close to his ears:

"Morning Star! O Morning Star!"

Then Morning Star sent his voice ringing among the tree-tops.

"*Qu'appelle?*"

Often as a boy he had hailed the *voyageurs* as they came up the river to his father's lodge, and heard them answer in these words: "*Qu'appelle?* Who calls?" and he had answered: "It is I!"

But no answer came to him now; only a sighing wind in the trees and the sob of the water under his canoe. Again he shouted, and in the silence his voice floated back to him:

"*Qu'appelle! Qu'appelle!*"

Afraid and wondering he sat, and as he called and listened the moon rose, and all that dismal place was changed. The trees stood like lighted torches, and there, an arrow's length beyond, the thickets opened, the stream merged into a broad flowing river, and in the distance the lights of the village twinkled like fireflies. His journey was nearly over.

Darkness was lifting from the plains as Morning Star came to the village; mist rose from the river, and in the east the sky was red and gold. There was smoke in the air, and silence over the village. "They are asleep," thought Morning Star. "I could slip in quietly, and when she wakes I shall be there, waiting."

He drew his canoe into the little cove below the notched poplar. As he climbed the bank it seemed to him that he could see the Little One standing beneath the tree, as she

129

had often stood, with her head touching its rough brown bark. But when he got there he saw nothing but the soft shreds of mist drifting between the branches. He followed the well-worn track to the village. As he went he heard a strange sound; voices lifted in a wailing cry, many of them together. The heart of Morning Star turned over, and his feet grew heavy so that he stood still among the poplar trees, while the weeping voices rose higher and louder and the air was filled with sorrow.

When at last he came to the lodge where his friends lived, he knew the story they had to tell. "The Little One has passed," they said. "She has passed into the Hereafter." Her father came with tears to meet him, and Morning Star put by his own grief to comfort the old man.

"She is not gone," he said. "Behold, as I came by the poplar she stood near me, though I was too blind to see clearly. Her body is dead—but she lives. She will never be lost to you."

Then he asked them how the Little One died, and they told him that the fever had taken her while she counted the days to his coming.

"Tonight before moonrise she called thee," they said. "Three times she spoke thy name. And as the moon rose she died."

Then Morning Star remembered the spirit voice, and although his eyes shed tears for the lost face of his bride, his heart was at peace because in her passing she had come to him.

130

"I go," he said to his friends. "This place will see me no more. Yet do not think of me in sadness; for though we made no wedding-feast I go not alone. Her spirit will be with me, to guide and to counsel; there shall be no parting, until the day when I stand beside her in the land that is beyond the setting sun. Farewell."

His canoe rode out on the river's stream. Into the sunrise it vanished, and as it went the watchers from the village fancied they saw a second figure seated in the craft, her shadowy paddle keeping time with his. Perhaps it was only the sun shining through the morning mists; nobody knows. Only they saw Morning Star no more; but they named the river the Qu'appelle, in memory of the two whose spirits met at moonrise on that night long ago.

White Men's Stories

It was a long time since the Gitche Manitou had created his garden. It was still a very wild place; but here and there parts of it began to bloom and yield harvest. Most of the increase was due to the white men, who worked very hard. They built cities, they sowed great wheat-fields and planted orchards, and they brought priests and nuns from their own country to teach the brown men how to be holy.

They didn't always do the right thing, but they tried hard. When the Gitche Manitou walked in the garden and saw what they were doing, he shook his head and sighed . . . and then he smiled.

"They are only children, after all," said the Gitche Manitou. "In time they will grow up."

And he rested; and sometimes as the people hurried to and fro they brushed against him, for they were very busy. And he said to himself:

"It does not matter. They will come this way again."

133

The Little Gray Man

There was a time, before the story of Canada began to be
written, when a big stretch of country reaching from the
Atlantic coasts of Nova Scotia and Cape Breton to the
south-east shores of the Saint Lawrence River was inhabited
by a tribe of people called the Micmacs. Like other Indian
races, they gave names to their rocks and rivers and mountains that described the kind of places they were; so when
they came to a great rounded piece of land sticking out
into the water, they called it End of the Land, or in Micmac
language, "Gaspé", and so it is to this day.

Now the schoolbooks say that Gaspé is a peninsula, which sounds very dull; but when you go there you will find it a wonderful place of cliffs and crags, of coves and mountains, of sandy beaches and tiny fishing hamlets; and around its shores cling tales of dwarfs, gnomes, giants, angels, phantom ships, and buried treasure. Exciting things have happened upon the coasts of Gaspé, and as you walk or ride there you feel a shivery wriggle in your spine, like the one you got when you were very small and woke up on Christmas morning to see your stocking full of strange shapes. Perhaps an old fisherman will tell you a story, sitting by his boat on the shore; perhaps, if he does, this is the one he'll tell.

Just where the northern shore of Gaspé curves towards the Gulf of Saint Lawrence, there stand two mountains so close to the shore that if you stood at the foot of them you could throw a rubber ball into the sea. They are called the Sauteux, and beneath them many a good ship has crashed to its death, for the coast is strewn with sharp rocks, some of them half covered with water so that you cannot know how large they are. The fisherfolk are afraid to walk there at night; lights go flickering over the rocks, as though ghostly lanterns were being carried to and fro, and then people speak under their breath and the children keep close to their mothers and fathers, for these, they say, are the spirits of lost sailors looking for the treasure they buried there long years ago.

Back in the early eighteenth century it was—nearly one hundred and fifty years after Jacques Cartier had set the lilies of France waving from Gaspé cliffs. The fishing boats

136

from France used to do a brisk trade then, as our Canadian fishermen do today, catching cod along the narrow shores from Cap-aux-Renards to the inlet of Gaspé Bay.

One of these boats belonged to a merchant named Roselle, and aboard it were two sailors whose names we will say were Jacques and Jean. They were not very good men, and they had signed on as sailors in the fishing smack because they had a bad reputation in their own country and thought it best to leave. Also, they had stolen from a wealthy jeweller a box containing a lot of gold pieces, and with this, they thought, they could make a start in the new land across the sea. Naturally Monsieur Roselle, who was a God-fearing man, did not know all this, otherwise he would certainly have put Jacques and Jean off the vessel before she started.

They set sail from the little port of Honfleur in Normandy, and for many stormy weeks they tossed between sea and sky on the great Atlantic. Never had the captain seen so much rough weather; and all the time, if he had only know it, *le bon Dieu* was trying to warn him that he had bad company aboard. Like many of us the captain was too busy with his own affairs to stop and think about *le bon Dieu*; so all he did was to complain about the dirty weather and the stupidity of the crew. You may be sure that Jacques and Jean were very stupid indeed, for they never wanted to be sailors at all, and cared for nothing but the precious box of gold which between them they managed to hide from the curious eyes of the others.

At last they sighted the rocky coast of Gaspé.

"Thank God," said the skipper, thinking of *le bon Dieu*

now that he was getting his own way. "Thank God we have arrived safely."

But he spoke too soon; for as their ship drew near the land a terrible thunderstorm rolled up, and the sea roared like a dragon, flinging huge waves over the deck so that some of the sailors were washed overboard before they could find so much as a rope to cling to. The skipper did his best, but the ship was beyond the help of mortals; tossed like a feather in the trough of the great waves, she was thrown against the edge of a half-covered reef and split from stem to stern.

The skipper, who was a brave man in spite of his grumbling, went down with his ship, and all his crew with him except one little sailor-boy and the man Jean. Jacques would have been saved too if he had not been so anxious about the box of gold; but when he tried to swim in the icy water the box dragged him under and he drowned. Jean and the sailor-boy clung to a piece of wood broken from the ship, and after hours of battering in the waves they were flung on the beach more dead than alive. The sun came up and warmed them, and after a while they lighted a fire with some driftwood and dried their clothes. The sea was quiet after the storm, but no life stirred on it; ship and crew had vanished completely.

"What shall we do?" cried the little sailor. "We shall starve in this strange country."

"Wait," said Jean, who had been prowling up and down the beach, "there is something over yonder that may help us."

138

Near the water's edge lay a square dark object. Jean lifted it, brushed off the wet sand, and there was the box of gold.

"Ah-ha," said he, "we shan't starve while we have this. In here are more gold pieces than you have ever dreamed of; enough to buy food for the king's army. You and I will be rich, my lad."

"How can we buy food if there is no one to sell to us?" cried the sailor-boy. "Gold pieces won't help us in this wild place."

Jean looked about; certainly it wasn't very promising. Huge gray cliffs rose up behind them, encircling the shore as far as they could see; the only things that lived were the great gulls that wheeled and cried overhead.

"There will be fisherfolk along the shore," said Jean. "I tell you what we will do. You stay here and guard the treasure, and I'll go and find food and shelter. Then I'll come back for you."

But the sailor didn't like that at all, and begged to be taken too.

"Nonsense," said Jean, "the box is too heavy to carry over these rocks. Besides, I'll do better without you dragging along."

With that he marched off, and the little sailor was left sitting on the treasure-box, feeling very lonely and miserable. The gulls flew down quite close and their bright fierce eyes frightened him; he threw pebbles at them, and they rose up with harsh screams and flapped their wings horribly.

"How lonely it is," thought the little sailor, whose name was Batiste. "How I wish someone would come and sit with me."

As the thought went through his head he saw a puff of white smoke sail past him, and thinking the fire had burnt up again he looked round quickly. On the sand behind him stood a little gray man looking down at him. Batiste stood up, quite confused, for he wasn't used to having his wishes granted so fast.

"I—I beg your pardon," he said timidly, not knowing what else to say.

"What for?" said the little gray man. His voice went *pop!* like a cork coming out of a bottle, and his sharp eyes snapped and twinkled.

Batiste couldn't think what for, so he said nothing; but he stared at the little man, for he had never seen anyone quite like him. His pointed cap was gray, and his hair was just like the gray wool Batiste's grandmother knitted his socks with—stiff and wiry; his beard was the same, and his face was quite pale and very round, like a ball. Batiste didn't pay much attention to the rest of him because his face kept changing shape; first, as I said, it was round, and then quite suddenly it pulled out like a piece of elastic and became long and thin; then it was square like a box, and then quite tiny, with sharp corners. Batiste shut his eyes because it made him feel dizzy; when he opened them the face was round again and the little man was smiling.

"Never seen me before, have you?" he said pleasantly.

Batiste said no, he hadn't.

"You will again, though," said the little man, and he sat himself down, cross-legged, on the box of gold.

"Where's your friend?"

He asked the question so abruptly that Batiste jumped as though a pin had stuck into him.

"He—he went along there," pointing along the shore.

"H'm," said the gray man, and shut his face up like an umbrella. He sat so long without moving that Batiste thought he was asleep and moved nearer to see; but as he stooped, the little man opened out his face again and remarked sharply:

"Beautiful weather, isn't it?"

Batiste didn't know what to say to this, so he nodded, and then ventured to ask:

"Do you live here?"

"Here and there," said the gray man, adding with a twinkle. "*There* mostly." He twisted round on the box and jerked his thumb towards the mountain.

"Oh," said Batiste, staring at it. "Isn't it cold up there?"

"Not as cold as it is in the sea," said the little man, and he looked at Batiste sharply and poked him in the ribs with a spiky forefinger. "All lost, eh?"

Batiste understood that he meant the wrecked ship, and nodded.

"All except me and Jean," he said.

"Jean." The gray man got up and shook himself like a puppy. "He is not good, that one." He tapped the treasure-box. "Know what's in here?"

Batiste hesitated. "Gold, Jean said."

"Ah," said the little man, and wagged his head till his hat fell off. Picking it up, he stuck it on Batiste's head instead of his own, remarking: "Keep you warm."

And indeed Batiste, who had been shivering in the wet salt wind, suddenly felt as though he were sitting in front of a blazing log fire, toasting his toes and eating hot chestnuts. He was so taken up with this new feeling that he did not hear the little man talking; so presently he got a dig in the ribs that sent him sprawling on the ground.

"Didn't you hear what I said?" demanded the little gray man.

Batiste sat up, rubbing himself. "I'm very sorry," he said, "but your hat—" At that moment he found that the hat had disappeared, and when he looked round to see what had become of it he was astonished to see it perched again on its owner's head.

"You were saying?" said the gray man politely.

Batiste got up. "I wish you'd stop playing jokes on me," he said crossly. "I don't know where I'm at. And that's a fact."

"You don't know much," said the gray man, but he said it so kindly that Batiste couldn't be offended. Suddenly he picked up the box of gold and tucked it under his arm.

"Come on," he said, and walked off briskly. Batiste called after him, but the little man only beckoned, and walked on faster than ever. Batiste ran after him.

"Look," he said when he caught up with the gray man, "you mustn't take that box away. Jean will beat me if it isn't there when he comes back."

142

"He won't come back," said the little man, and began to whistle cheerfully.

Batiste asked "How do you know?" but the gray man went on whistling, and at that moment they turned a sharp corner of the mountain and found themselves in a little cove, quite hidden from the shore. The gray man put the box down, walked towards the steep side of the mountain, and disappeared.

It sounds foolish, but it happened like that. He was gone as completely as though the earth had swallowed him; in fact, after searching for half an hour or so Batiste decided that was the only explanation.

"I had better find out where I was before," he thought to himself, "or Jean will be very angry." So he bent down to pick up the box. It seemed to have stuck in the ground; he tugged, but it did not move. Batiste got his hands under it and pulled with all his might; it was no use, he couldn't stir it. "Oh dear," he said out loud. "Whatever shall I do?"

While he stood looking at the box, quite downcast, he noticed a puff of smoke coming up from the sand. He turned round, and there stood the little gray man with a pickaxe in his hand.

"What a hurry you're in," he said calmly. "Why didn't you wait for me?"

Batiste was so angry that he stamped his foot.

"Give me back my box!" he shouted. "I won't stay here any longer. You've played tricks on me and stolen my box; you've no right to keep it."

"Neither have you," said the gray man, "nor Jean either,

for that matter. Here." He pushed the pickaxe into Batiste's hand. "Dig."

"What for?" Batiste was still angry.

"You'll see," said the gray man, and he smiled so pleasantly that Batiste's anger melted. He took the pickaxe and began to dig while the little man watched. The hole grew very quickly. Batiste hadn't been at it for more than a minute or so before there was a pit in the rocky ground deep enough to put an ox-cart in.

"That's enough," said the gray man. "We'll put the box in."

Batiste didn't think much of this, but he thought that if he interfered, the gray man might vanish altogether and leave him alone without the box of gold. So he said nothing, but helped to lower the box into the pit.

"Now we'll fill it in," said the gray man; but when Batiste took up the pickaxe he stopped him.

"Don't bother with that. Turn round."

Batiste obeyed. When he looked again the hole was filled in and the sand lay over it as smoothly as though it had never been touched.

"Much quicker, don't you think?" said the gray man cheerfully. "Now come on."

"Where are we going now?" Batiste took hold of the gray man's coat so that he should not vanish and leave him behind.

"I am going to take you to the top of the mountain," said the little man. "Hold on tight."

With that he took Batiste firmly by the arm, and sud-

144

denly, whoof!—they were standing on top of the mountain, and the sea rolled like a green valley beneath them.

"Look," said the gray man, and he turned Batiste around. Below them on the other side of the mountain lay a beautiful country of fields and woods and rivers; at their feet grew patches of pink mallows, clinging to the rocky soil and lifting their heads to the sun as though they were happy to be alive. Batiste could see white daisies and clover in the fields, and other gay-coloured flowers that he did not know.

"Like it?" asked the little man. Batiste nodded; he was thinking that it looked a little bit like home, lying there so peacefully in the sunshine, and for a minute he was homesick and wanted his grandmother, who was so kind to him and knitted him socks and scarves. The gray man seemed to guess how Batiste was feeling, for he put his hand on the lad's shoulder and said very kindly:

"Would you like to live there, Batiste?"

Batiste wondered afterwards how the gray man knew his name; but at the time it seemed quite natural, and he nodded and said:

"I think I should like it very much. But I should be lonely all by myself."

The gray man felt in his pockets and brought out a little mirror.

"Take this with you," he said. "The first person you meet whose face is reflected in this mirror will be your companion for the rest of your life."

Batiste said "But where am I going?"

145

"Ah," said the gray man, "I can't tell you that. I can tell you how to start, though." He took off his cap and put it once more on Batiste's head. "This cap will protect you from whatever might do you harm. Go down the mountain by this path you see in front of us. When you get to the bottom I will wave, and you'll find yourself walking along a narrow road. Follow it until you meet a man carrying a fishing-net. He'll take you to his home and look after you. From that time on you must manage for yourself."

"But what about Jean," said Batiste, "and the treasure?"

The gray man sat down on a rock and looked at Batiste for a long time without speaking. Batiste noticed then that his eyes were not gray like the rest of him, but blue like the sea, like the sky, like the little wild iris that grew in the valleys below. The gray man spoke.

"Batiste, you are an ignorant little sailor-boy. You don't read or write very well, you can only do the simplest sums, and you don't know anything about the big world you live in. But you know one thing that is better than all these, and because you know it I have brought you up here. Jean knows nothing except his own greediness, and so he has lost all that he thought he had. The treasure will stay where it is until someone who knows how to use it comes along. But you, my little Batiste," the gray man stood up, and he was taller than Batiste had imagined him, "you have found out that things happen to people that can't be explained in schoolbooks, and that it is never safe to say 'That *can't* happen.' *Anything* can happen if folks have

146

simple hearts and believe in *le bon Dieu*. Now you must start."

Batiste said: "Shall I ever see you again?" for he felt suddenly sad.

The gray man smiled. "When the sun touches the tip of Sauteux on his way down to the west, look up to this mountain. I shall be here, and I shall wave to you."

Everything happened to Batiste just as the gray man had told him. He followed the path down the mountain, and when he got to the bottom he turned and looked up. The gray man was standing where Batiste had left him; he raised his arm and waved. Instantly a gray mist dropped over the mountain, hiding everything except the narrow red-gravelled road that led away from Batiste into the fields. All day he walked, with the sweet scent of the grass and clover in his nostrils; and at evening he met the fisherman and went home with him as the gray man had said.

How Batiste met the fisherman's daughter, and saw her face in his little mirror and married her and was very happy all his life is another story, and you may write it for yourself; but he never forgot the little gray man, and often at sunset he would look up to the Sauteux Mountains and see a gray mist rising like a puff of smoke. Then he knew that the gray man was waving his hand.

And the treasure? Well, as I have said, people don't like to walk among the rocks below Sauteux after dark, for Jean and his evil companions still return to look for the box of gold. But the little gray man must be keeping guard, for

147

sometimes stones are dropped from the mountain-top on the heads of folk who go prying too near the cove where the treasure is buried, and they say that if you light a fire at a certain spot on the beach it will turn into a puff of smoke and sail off into the sea. Perhaps some day the right person will come by, and then the gold will be found and the little gray man will be seen no more. It may be; no one knows.

The Silver Bullet

Once upon a time (since this is the way to begin all good tales) there was a place called Baldoon. It was a way off in a corner, where the big silver River St. Clair runs shining to the Lakes, and at that time the country all round about it was called Upper Canada, and it was very wide and bare and desolate, not a bit like the comfortable fat farms and villages we see by the highways today.

Now the people who lived in Baldoon in these far-off

days were poor folk who had only the little log huts they lived in and a few bits of home-made furniture to call their own—except their farms, and *they* weren't much good to them as you'll see. Everybody had fifty acres of land to begin with, so that there could be no fighting or squabbling over whose farm was biggest; but it was astonishing how soon they began to buy and sell to each other, exchanging an acre here or a field there for some extra corn, or potatoes, or sometimes for fine-spun bits of cloth woven by the wives and daughters. Thus after a while it chanced that some of the settlers had fat, prosperous farms, well-tilled and pastured, while others only had miserable skinny little strips of ground, hardly fit to grow even a pumpkin on. So it is always, wherever people get together, and so it will be always until folk learn to keep themselves to themselves and leave other folk to their own business.

In this muddy little settlement of Baldoon—for it was very muddy; it sat down in a hollow like the dip in the palm of your hand, and when it rained all the water ran down from the land above it and lay in dirty puddles in people's gardens—in this settlement, as I began to say, there lived two families whose doings were very strange. No one knew why they acted as they did, and no one connected the one with the other.

One family was called McDonald, and in it was John McDonald, who was a sturdy rosy-cheeked Scotsman, and his wife Annie, who came from a little island off the coast of Scotland. The name of the island was Tobermory, and Annie was very homesick for it sometimes; she used to sit

looking over the mud flats of Baldoon and say in a kind
of chant:

> *Tobermory, Tobermory!*
> *The hills all purple, and*
> *The sea all blue—*
> *Why did I leave Tobermory?*

And she was very sad. But then other days she would be
brisk and cheerful, and Floss their daughter would say:

"The sun's out, Mother! Maybe there'll be buds on the
trees today!"

For it was early April, and one of those cold Ontario
springs when the wind howls like a wolf and frightens the
little warm breezes away, so that everything stays bleak and
brown and the trees shiver in all their bare black branches.

The McDonalds lived in a small square frame house on
the banks of the Channel Ecarté—a yellowy-brown creek-
ish sort of river that flowed sluggishly through the Baldoon
country. They hadn't much of a farm, for they'd had very
ill luck for the past few years; their crops had been poor
and hadn't paid their way, so that they had to buy food
from their neighbours and often sold their land to get
money to pay for the food—little parts of it at a time, a bit
of bush here and a square of pasture there—till there was
very little of it left.

Yet John McDonald worked hard, and so did his wife
Annie and his daughter Floss.

"Good's bound to come if you work hard and live
honest," John would say, smoking his corn pipe of an

evening in front of the crackling white birch logs that burned in the stone fireplace.

But it didn't come to the McDonalds, and after a while some very queer stories began to get about, the way stories will when people do anything that their neighbours don't do.

"Did ye pass the house on the Channel tonight?" people would murmur to one another on their way home from corn-husks or quilting bees.

"Deed and I did not," would be the reply.

"I did," one bolder than the rest would say. "*I* passed the house on the Channel, and all dark it was. Not a candle's flicker in the windows. And do you know what I heard?"

Then the neighbours would creep close about the bold one and whisper:

"Tell us! Tell us!"

And the bold one would whisper back, and the neighbours would shiver and shake like the leaves on the poplar trees along the banks of the Channel Ecarté.

"Ay! Ay!" they would say. "The house has the evil eye!"

That was the tale that went round. Meanwhile the poor McDonalds suffered dreadful losses. Their cows and horses died without anyone knowing why, their corn-ears blackened with the rot and their potatoes had scabs on them; and always at dusk, when everybody else's house had little yellow lights dancing in the windows, the McDonalds' house would be dim and silent. What did they do at nights? Did they sit in the darkness weaving black magic? Did

152

they brew evil concoctions over the red-hot ashes of pine-needles, as some people said they had seen witches do? It was all very mysterious and frightening, and mothers wouldn't let their little girls and boys go past the house alone.

Now the other family I spoke about a few minutes ago was called Mugan. That wasn't their real name but I won't tell it because one of the families might still be alive and read this story and be angry. There was an old woman Mugan, and her grandson Neil who worked the farm, and they lived in a Long, Low Log House at the opposite end of the settlement, where the mud seemed flatter, yellower, and oozier than in any other part. The Mugans were not very much liked because they were sour-faced, silent people and they looked dirty. They mightn't have *been* dirty, but they looked it; and you know that when *you* look dirty you have to go and wash, even if you think you're as clean as clean. No one had the courage to tell the Mugans to go and wash, and so they kept on looking dirty, and being sour-faced and silent.

Unlike the McDonalds, the people of the Long, Low Log House had splendid luck with their farm. Everything they touched flourished. The corn was fat and luscious on the cob, the pumpkins and potatoes were twice as big as anyone else's, and their cows gave so much milk that half the inhabitants of Baldoon bought their cream and butter from the Log House instead of bothering to make it themselves. So the Mugans made money, but you would never have known it, because they went about looking just as

153

slatternly as ever. The shingles on the Log House roof needed repairing, and the door swung crazily on broken hinges, just as though they hadn't anything at all. The old woman hoarded the money, people said.

Between the McDonalds on the Channel Ecarté and the Mugans on the mud flats there was a funny sort of feeling, like you have when someone won't play with you. Once the Log House people had wanted to buy some of John's land, and he had refused to sell it to them. He didn't know just why he had done this; it gave him a queer feeling, he said, to be thinking of that long-jawed fellow walking through his fields. But the Mugans had been very angry, and had not spoken to the McDonalds since.

Now what was it that was going on at the house on the Channel Ecarté? Why did they sit in the dark at night and seem afraid to go out by day? I'll tell you.

It all began a long while ago—in fact, just after the quarrel with the Mugans. Floss, with a dozen or so other young ladies, had gone to a neighbour's to help pick over straw for weaving. Out of the straw, during the long winter months, the women and children would weave the broad-brimmed hats that protected their husbands and fathers through the summer harvests. The girls worked in the barn, where the straw lay in soft, shining piles, smelling of sun and rain. It was just like a party; someone had brought corn cakes and clover honey, and the girls wore their prettiest frocks, for the straw was clean, not like the dusty cornstalks at huskings. They chattered and laughed and played games and sang, the same as young ladies do

154

today when they get together. Some of the songs they sang
were very old ones, learned from their grandfathers and
grandmothers, and some they made up as they went along.
Here is one of them:

> *"Straw yellow, straw gold,*
> *I want to have my fortune told."*
> *"Maiden, maiden, moon in your eyes,*
> *You'll be wed when the thistledown flies."*
>
> *"Straw yellow, straw gold,*
> *What shall I do when I grow old?"*
> *"Maiden, maiden, sun in your eyes,*
> *Ask no questions and get no lies."*

The barn was made of logs, and across the top of it,
inside, poles were laid on the beams from side to side,
forming a loft where flax or corn-stalks could be stored.
Just now it was empty, except for a few bundles of old
straw. The fun was at its merriest; one of the girls, a rosy
maid called Heather, told how she had got the best of
Moody Miller, the meanest man in Baldoon.

"Moody Miller! Moody Miller!" chanted the girls.
"Heather Bell beat Mean Moody Miller!" And they laughed
and were very gay.

Cr-rash!

Everybody jumped a foot in the air. Right down the
middle of the pile of straw they were working on lay one
of the poles from the roof. It had just missed Floss Mc-
Donald's big toe, where she had stuck her foot out while
she worked.

"That's funny!" said Molly McGee, whose father owned

155

the barn. "I never knew one of those poles to come loose before."

With a good deal of difficulty the girls lifted the pole and got it back in its place, one climbing up the ladder at the side of the mow and pushing the pole into place while the rest held it up. At last it lay again across the beams, and the girls turned back to their straw-picking. The chatter rose merrily.

Cr-r-rash!

Another pole!

This time it came down end-up, struck on the floor just at Floss's elbow, and slithered slowly to the ground, knocking over the jar of honey that belonged to Betty the miller's daughter.

"Oh, my honey jar, my honey jar! What will my mother say?"

The little brown jar was broken in tiny pieces. Betty began to cry; some of the others comforted her, but the bigger girls stood looking up, trying to see what made the poles fall down. There was nothing unusual to be seen, so presently they scrambled and scraped and climbed again, got the fallen pole back to its place and went on working as before. But now they did not chatter or laugh.

Crash! *Crash!* CRASH!

The workers leaped up and scattered in all directions like flurries of white hen's feathers. Every pole in the barn had fallen and they were lying piled one on top of another, with the yellow straw pushed all ways and poking up between them.

156

The girls fled madly down the orchard path to the farm-house crying out that the barn was bewitched. They poured out the whole story to Farmer Magee who had just come in from the fields. He went at once to the barn, the girls tiptoeing at a safe distance behind him. He stepped through the big door. Every pole was lying in its place on the beams, and the straw was neatly stacked as it had been when the girls sat working at it.

"You had a bad dream, children," the farmer said to the astonished young ladies.

But Floss knew it wasn't a dream, because when she got home that night she found a little splinter of pine-wood in the toe of her left shoe. It had come off one of the poles, and when she took it out her big toe hurt her as if the splinter had stuck into it.

After that things happened quickly, queerer and queerer things. The McDonalds tried to hide them, but the tales got about. People said that all the pots and pans in the house on the Channel Ecarté had come alive. "What a terrible thing!" they said. "Your own frying pan leaping off the fire and hitting you on the nose, the knives and spoons walking round the room as though they had feet on them, and soup ladles giving you a beating when you went to bed at night." Things were quiet when it was dark, and so the family did not light the candles after dusk, but felt their way about as well as they could, creeping to bed with many a shiver and shake in the black, silent house.

And this wasn't all. Stones flew in at the windows with none to throw them; the dog wouldn't cross the threshold, but lay shivering outside; all the crops in the garden died, and the cows' milk dried up. It went on and on, and the family used to hear feet tramping up and down outside the house; but when they went to the door no one was there. It got very bad indeed, and bit by bit the evil doings spread, to this neighbour and that, until at last the only house in the whole of the Baldoon Settlement that was free of trouble was the Long Low Log House. *Its* inhabitants went about as freely as ever, their crops and cattle grew fatter and fatter, and the bags of money hoarded by the old woman must have grown very heavy, because now the Mugans were selling food to nearly the whole colony.

John felt that this state of things could not go on. Someone had told him about a wise man who lived at Long Point, several days' journey away on the shores of Lake Erie, who was said to have great power over witches and sorcerers. John didn't know whether his troubles were caused by witches; but he decided to go and see the wise man, whose name was Doctor Troyer, and ask for his help.

So one morning very early John kissed his wife and daughter, took the only horse left in the stable and a knapsack of food, and rode away with Pastor McDorman, the good minister of the settlement, to keep him company and fend off the evil spirits. The Pastor had his book open on his saddle-front, and as they rode he sang hymns and recited prayers so that no bad thing should stop them on their journey.

All went well until they began to ride through the Long Woods—heavy swampy bush-country it was, and the mud

158

on the trail sucked the horses' feet under and made their progress very slow. No sooner had they entered the bush than they began to hear weird noises. Owls screamed over their heads, bats swooped on them from low wet branches, and around and before them they heard the dismal baying of wolves. John McDonald shook in his big riding-boots, but he said not a word; and Pastor McDorman sang louder and prayed faster, while the clamour about them grew terrific. Shouts and cries pursued them, as if invisible enemies were on their track—shrieks as of people in torment, moans, beating of drums, and all kinds of horrifying sounds. The Pastor's singing was quite drowned out, but John saw his mouth opening and shutting and knew he was doing his duty as a brave man should. All that night they rode through the bush, and terror surrounded them; but as dawn rose up behind them they came out at last into calm open country, and the horrid sounds died away.

Doctor Troyer lived in a little log house down a sandy road. As the riders drew near they saw a small orchard of apple and cherry trees, already showing pale green buds; orchards were rare in those parts, and John remarked that the Doctor must indeed be a magician to have apple trees like that. Over the door of the house were two crossed horse-shoes—"To keep out the Evil One," the minister said. They tied their horses to an apple tree and knocked at the door. It was opened by a girl of about fifteen, a thin, queer-looking creature.

John said: "We have come to see Doctor Troyer. Is he at home?"

The girl looked at them for a second or two without answering. She had pale-coloured eyes, and they seemed to look through you and out the other side.

At last she spoke, and her voice made the minister think of the big bells on the church he had left in Scotland. It was deep and it rang in your head like the humming of a top.

"My father is waiting for you," she said.

John's eyes opened wide at this, for he had not sent any word to the good Doctor to say they were coming, and so how would he know? However, he said nothing, for he was a little afraid of the Troyer girl's pale eyes, and he half thought the minister was too for all his book learning. So they went inside, and there they were met by the most majestic old man they had ever seen. He was tall and straight as a poplar tree; his hair, white as fine wool, streamed over his shoulders, and his beard reached below his waist. He had eyes like a hawk's, and he was handsome and terrifying.

He spoke to the travellers gently, and their fear left them when he smiled, for then his face was mild and gentle. To their astonishment he knew their story before they told it.

"I saw it in the stars," said he; nor did he explain any further.

"Sir, can you help us?" asked John. "We are sore beset and do not know where to turn."

Doctor Troyer shook his head several times, very slowly.

"It is not easy to avert the power of evil. Even now,

160

while you sit here, your outbuildings are being burned to the ground."

"My outbuildings!" cried John. "My barn? My stable?"

"That is so," said the Doctor. He got up and went towards the inner room. "I will call my daughter. She may be able to do something for you." He tapped three times on the door, and out came the strange girl who had let them in.

"Eileen," said the Doctor, "tell what you know."

The girl Eileen looked at them all—at John, at Mr. McDorman, at her father. Then she shook her head.

"I know nothing," she said.

Doctor Troyer went to her and put the tips of his fingers against her forehead; then he said again:

"Eileen, tell what you know."

This time the girl shut her eyes, and seemed to be in pain. She pushed her father's hand away fretfully and said as before:

"I know nothing."

Then the Doctor beckoned to John. "Put your hand on her forehead." John hesitated, the girl looked at him so fiercely; but the Doctor nodded to him sharply, so he went up to her and put his hand against her forehead. She cried out as though he had struck her, and then she said, each word dragged out of her:

"I see a long, low log house."

John was so surprised he almost took his hand away; but the Doctor shook his head, and signed to him to keep quiet. Eileen spoke again.

161

"I see an old woman. She is evil. Her heart is evil. There lies all your trouble."

She shook off John's hand, and would not say another word.

"But what am I to do?" cried John.

The Doctor looked at him gravely and said:

"There are two things that you must do. First, you must shoot the gray goose with the black head that feeds among your fowls."

John wanted to ask how the Doctor knew about the gray goose, but he was afraid of Eileen; so he said meekly:

"I have tried. But I never managed to hit it."

"Because you shot with a lead bullet," said the Doctor. "Lead will never touch that bird. You must shoot with a bullet of silver."

John said: "I have no silver bullet."

"Then you must make one," said the Doctor. "Can you overcome evil without paying for it?"

And because he had spoken sharply, he smiled, and John took heart again.

"What else must I do to avert the power of evil?"

"Ah," said the Doctor, "that you must find out for yourself. But I'll give you a hint. It is a good thing to slay hatred; it is a better thing to turn it into love."

And he sent them on their way, and would take no payment, though John urged it upon him.

Homeward rode John and the minister, and nothing harmed them; when they got there they found that the outbuildings had been burned, at the exact time the Doctor

162

had said. The family were in great distress; but John said:

"Don't worry about it. Tomorrow everything will be all right."

That night, after everyone else had gone to bed, he opened the cupboard where they kept their few treasures and took out a candlestick which had belonged to his great-grandmother. It was sterling silver and very costly, and John prized it more than anything he owned. In the quiet hours while the family slept he melted it down, and out of it he moulded a bullet, smooth and glittering as a bright pebble. Early in the morning he took his gun and the silver bullet and stole down to the creek where the geese were feeding. There was the gray goose, its black head bobbing above the rest, getting the best food as it always did. John lifted his gun, took careful aim, and fired. He heard a strange, wild cry; he saw the gray goose flutter into the bushes, its left wing trailing broken on the ground. But when he ran to look for it, the bird had vanished. Not a feather of it was to be found.

John went home to breakfast, and the sky seemed bluer, the birds sang more merrily than when he had gone out.

"That's the first thing," he said to himself. "Now I wonder what the second can be?"

As he came near the house Floss ran out to meet him.

"Father, there has been an accident at the Long Low Log House! Mrs. Mugan has broken her arm—and there's no one to set it."

Now John knew a little about medicine, and the neighbours often called him when someone was hurt or ill. But he had never gone to the Long Low Log House.

"When did it happen?" he asked Floss.

"Just a few minutes ago. No one knows how it came about, and Mrs. Mugan won't tell."

John looked at his breakfast ready for him on the table, and sniffed the good smell of coffee and bacon. Then he took his little black bag from the shelf by the kitchen door and went down the road to the Long Low Log House.

The old woman sat by the fire, her left arm hanging useless at her side. Not a word did she utter as John set the arm and bound it in a sling; but when he had packed his lint and bandages away in the little black bag and was moving to the door, she spoke.

"Neighbour."

John turned. The old woman beckoned with her right hand. "Come nearer."

John went close to her chair. She put a skinny finger on his arm. "Yon was a kind turn you did me. Mugans can hate and Mugans can love; you shall see." Lifting herself by the arm of the chair, she took from the mantel a small metal box and held it out to John. "Open it."

John took it and pressed the lid open. Inside was the silver bullet.

"Say nothing," said the old woman before John could speak. "Take it home and keep it for your grandchildren. There's peace on your house from this time onward."

The next day when John went to see how the broken arm was getting on, he found the door swinging wide open, the hearth cold, the whole place deserted and lifeless. The Mugans had vanished, lock, stock, and barrel.

From that time forward the luck of the settlement turned; farms gave crops, cattle grew fat, and peace came to the house of the McDonalds as the old woman had said. But when John told the story to his grandchildren years afterwards, there were two things he was never quite sure about; first, whether he ever accomplished the second task set by the old Doctor, and second, whether the silver bullet really killed the gray goose.

What do you think?

The Seven Witches of Long Point

A long time ago, when our great-great (or great-great-great) grandparents came to this country, there was a certain spot of land where the Powers of Darkness held sway. No one knew why this was so. Perhaps it had been too rudely snatched from its Indian kinsfolk by the white people who came to live there; or perhaps it had stood empty and silent when the Red Men went away to other hunting grounds, and so the Evil Ones took it for their own.

This place was called Long Point, and it ran into Lake Erie in a thin flicker of land like a toad's tongue. On each side of it the cliffs curled back in a dark semi-circle, and no matter how brightly the sun shone the Point was always blurred and misty.

Now the Powers of Darkness had appointed as guardians over this piece of land seven witches. They were old and ugly and thin and scrawny, as witches must be who have their minds full of bad thoughts; and their names were Hit and Miss and Wrinkle and Scowl and Rags and Tatters and Trouble. Trouble was the leader of the troupe, and she looked like a cross school-teacher who straps her children. You'll find out what the others looked like as we go along.

The work of the seven witches was to see that the inhabitants of the Point got no chance to meet the Good People— those kind Spirits we all know about who keep the sun shining and the dew sparkling and who polish up the minds of men and women (and children too) and keep them clear and fresh and tidy, so that no nasty ideas get into the corners. The poor settlers didn't know what was wrong with them, but they did know that they couldn't go out after dark without falling into a swamp, nor walk through the woods in the early mornings without getting themselves covered with thorns and burrs and poison-ivy—and if you've ever had poison-ivy rash you'll know what uncomfortable things the witches could think up when they put their minds to it.

There was one person in Long Point who annoyed the witches very much. His name was Troyer, and he was a wise man of medicine who had read a great many books, all of them about witches. They were stacked on the shelves of his cabin from the floor to the ceiling, huge dusty things, each one weighing as much as a sack of wheat, with their names written in Latin across their backs. The witches couldn't read Latin and so they were angrier than ever, and used to sit in dark corners thinking up ways to harm and upset the good doctor.

They had to be careful, because as a matter of fact he was as clever as they were. Besides being a good man and going to church as often as he could (which frightened the witches very much), he knew a lot of Magic, and used to sing it to himself in the long winter evenings when the blizzards roared like black leopards over the lake, and the witches shivered on their slippery broomsticks and pulled their cloaks tighter over their skinny bones.

Here is one of the doctor's Magics:

> *Snow, hail, ice and rain,*
> *Mix me a draught of sorcerer's bane.*
> *Sneeze, freeze, shiver and shake—*
> *Drown, evil! Witches, quake!*

While the doctor said this Magic, he drew Things on the frosted window-pane with the nail of the little finger of his left hand. Every time he did this the witches caught dreadful colds in their heads, so that they had to stay at home with their red flannel thingummys on and their feet in hot mustard. The mustard burned them and the red flannel scratched them, and they sat up all night sneezing and saying spells so that no more Magic could come near them.

Now it happened that every year a great ball was held across the lake at a place called Dunkirk. This ball was given for the workers of the Powers of Darkness from all the country roundabout. No one ever saw the host, or knew where the invitations came from, but there were games and masques and dancing, and at midnight the most delicious food appeared on the tables, though no one came to serve it. The ball was looked forward to the whole year, and every witch, demon, pixie, sprite, goblin, ghost, and will-o'-the-wisp that respected itself would be there. Each year there was a great deal of rivalry over who would appear in the smartest clothes, the grandest carriage, or bring the costliest gift for the unseen host; the guests were so jealous of one another that it wasn't unusual for the whole affair to end up in a frightful battle, so that people at the Point would look across the Lake and say:

"What a terrible thunderstorm there is tonight!"

The Seven Witches were given great honour at the ball, first because they were old and skilful, and second because they were known to be so spiteful that even their own fellow-creatures were a bit afraid of them. You never knew when they might take a dislike to you and change you into a frog or a worm on the way home—which was so awkward to explain to one's family.

The story that I set out to tell you is about a particular year when the bad feelings between Doctor Troyer and the Seven Witches were at their worst. It was one of the stormiest winters anyone in the district could remember, even the Indians who had lived there all their lives; eight times the doctor had made his Magic, and eight times the witches caught colds. No wonder they peered anxiously

170

out of their windows each morning to see if spring had arrived; they even set a jar of honey outside their door when they went to bed, so that if she came in the night, cold and tired after her long journey from the south, she would see the little brown jar on the doorstep and say as she sipped from it:

"How kind of the witches to think of me! I must do something for them at once!"

You see how sly the old things were. They knew that if they had spring on their side they could bring down all sorts of trouble on the doctor: fevers and chills and agues, mumps, measles, whooping-cough, and pediculosis, and all the ailments that spring can give people if they're not on good terms with her.

However, as it happened spring upset their plans by coming in from a different direction and never going near the witches' house at all—the kind of trick she likes playing, being only a child after all and as fond of keeping April Fool's Day as you or I. So one morning the witches woke up to hear the water dripping gaily off the roof and the ice crunching and crackling in the lake below; and while they were hurrying into their dressing-gowns and taking their hair out of curlers, there was a loud rapping at the door and one of the neighbours stuck her head in and shouted:

"Have you heard the news? Spring's here!"

Just as though they hadn't ears and eyes of their own.

Well, that day the postman brought the invitations for the Dunkirk Ball. It was always held as soon as spring arrived; which made it rather hard on everyone's temper, owing to spring's never coming the same day two years running, so that you couldn't be sure when to have your evening clothes taken out of storage. The only safe way was to get them out very early; but of course no one ever did, and there was always a terrible scrambling into trunks and boxes and unwrapping of tissue paper—you could smell the moth balls all the way from Lake Erie to the River St. Clair, and people in the Baldoon Settlement, miles and miles away, sniffed the air and said among themselves:

"What a tremendous spring cleaning someone is doing this morning!"

Now it chanced that this year the Seven Witches were especially anxious to make a good appearance at the ball. There had been a little difficulty the year before over a Personage who had come from Detroit, a long way off, as a special Guest of Honour, and who had arrived in such magnificence that everybody else was completely put into the shade. Hit, Miss, Wrinkle, Scowl, Rags, Tatters, and Trouble had been overlooked as though they had been persons of no importance whatever, and had had to sit on wooden benches and eat their supper with common people like the Goblins and Ghosts, instead of occupying chairs of state at the head table as they usually did. They had not forgotten this, and had spent a good many evenings sitting round their great fireplace where the white birch logs spluttered and blazed, putting their wits together so that they could plan something impressive to give them back their lost dignity.

172

It was Hit who thought of it—little Hit, whose face was brown and wizened as a beech-nut, and who was so small that she could ride the winds on a piece of milk-thistle-down.

"What we need," said little Hit, "is a horse."

"A horse!" cried the others. "Where should we get a horse? And what good would it do?"

"Ah," said Hit, shaking her head, "you've forgotten, Sisters. Last year we were laughed at because we rode on broomsticks, as witches did thousands of years ago. We're behind the times. Broomsticks went out with hooped skirts. Don't you know that nowadays everyone wears crinolines? We must change our broomsticks for something more up-to-date."

"She's right, Sisters," spoke up Trouble, the leader. "Broomsticks are out. But where shall we get a horse?"

Hit had thought of that too. Beckoning with a thin brown finger no bigger than a grasshopper's claw, she drew the others close around her and whispered into Trouble's ear. Trouble whispered to Tatters; Tatters whispered to Rags; Rags whispered to Scowl; Scowl to Wrinkle; Wrinkle to Miss. Then all the witches rose up from their seven stools and cried:

"It shall be done!"

And on to their old-fashioned broomsticks they got, and off they whisked in a twinkling to the end of Long Point where Doctor Troyer lived.

Now the Doctor had a clever daughter called Eileen, and if she hadn't been out gathering May apples on this

173

particular morning, the thing that happened to her father would never have come about. Eileen could give the witches one look from her pale eyes (green they were like the colour of hazel-nuts in summer) and they would curl up as the maple leaves do when the hard frost bites them. But Wrinkle, who was smart about finding things out, and whose shape was exactly like a question mark, knew that Eileen had gone out early with her little reed basket and would not come back until the witches had worked their evil designs.

It was a sharp, sweet morning in early May, and all the world was out nesting. The birds muttered and clattered among the branches, and frogs sang in the marshes where the yellow kingcups were having their faces washed in dew. The witches rode high, not wanting to be seen by the folk busy at their Monday morning wash. When they came to the log cabin where Doctor Troyer lived they all hid in the tree-tops, except Hit who went boldly down the chimney. Because she was tiny she always had to do jobs of this kind, and sometimes she got very cross about it.

Going down a chimney is nasty dusty work, but Hit was used to it and had put on her overalls. The Doctor was eating his breakfast, taking great bites of corn-bread toast and great spoonfuls of porridge, all the time reading from a huge book propped up against the copper coffee-pot in front of him. The coffee-pot, which had belonged to the Doctor's grandmother and was therefore very fond of him, saw Hit coming down the chimney, and tried to warn his master by puffing steam into his face; but the Doctor was muttering a new Magic he had found in the book, and paid no attention.

Hit stole up behind the Doctor's chair, watched until he took an extra big spoonful of porridge, and then quick as a humming-bird she shinned up the back of the chair and tossed her cloak over the good man's head, tying it round his neck so tight that between it and the hot porridge he was swallowing, it was a wonder he didn't choke to death. Then Hit sat on his head and cried in a voice that sounded like the rattle of a door on a windy day:

> *Hey! hey! the deed is done!*
> *Good's over and bad's begun—*
> *Whee-ee-ee-ee!*

As she whistled the last word a little gust of wind came swishing round the open door and *pst!* up the chimney went Hit and the Doctor, just as though they'd been blown up by a rocket. *Plonk* they landed on the roof, and there were the other six witches doing a tap dance on their broomsticks: tink, tonk, bingabom-*bink*, while six woodpeckers drummed for them with their beaks.

"Got him," said Hit, and smacked the Doctor smartly on the head so that he rolled over in a dead faint. Then they seized him and propped him against the chimney, and while Rags and Tatters, who were the biggest and strongest of the seven, held him firmly, the others joined hands in a circle and chanted a Mystic Rhyme. I shouldn't like to tell you the words because you might try them yourself and there's no knowing what would happen; but if some day you take a long stick and poke it at a wasp's nest, and then

175

get your ear as close as you dare and listen very hard, you'll get a general idea of the thing.

They sang it seven times, and at the end of the seventh Trouble flung her broomstick into the air and shrieked:

"Horse! Horse! Horse!"

The others took up the cry, and they danced round the Doctor on their long pointed toes. If you can imagine all the cats you every saw screaming together at dead of night, you will know how these evil old ladies sounded.

But as they sang, peculiar things happened. First the air all round them turned bright scarlet, like the cheeks of a ripe apple. (You know what an uninteresting colour air usually is.) Next there was to be heard a sort of dull drumming and throbbing, as though some enormous engine had been started. This was the Powerhouse of Evil turning its wheels; every time something bad is going to happen, these wheels begin to move, and you can hear them if you keep quiet and think very hard. The trouble is that people don't think hard enough, and so they don't notice when the wheels begin, and so the bad things happen, as they did to Doctor Troyer.

Faster and faster danced the witches, and now they tore off their black coats and threw them over the Doctor, who still lay in his dead faint. As soon as the cloaks touched him the whole place—air, sky, earth, everything—went black as ink, and a terrible roll of thunder shook the little cabin so that its shingles rattled like loose teeth. It was all over in a second, the sky grew light again, and there on the roof-top, the black cloaks crumpled under his feet, stood a

176

beautiful white horse; his mane and tail were silver, and his nostrils were pink like the petals of a wild rose. When the witches saw him they clapped their hands and cried:

"Now we'll be the Guests of Honour at the Ball!"

They took the Horse home with them, making a halter out of their cloak-strings to lead him by. They weren't very polite to him, considering what a handsome creature he was. They poked at him with their broomsticks and kicked his legs with their sharp toes; they pulled his tail and shouted rude things at him.

"Gee up, Troyer!"

"Magic yourself out of this if you can!"

"Give us some Latin, Doctor!"

And so on.

As the time for the ball drew near, there was great bustle and stir among the Bad People of Lake Erie. Spinning-wheels purred, needles flew, gossamer rose to a terrible price, so that when the Good Fairies wanted some for their June wedding-veils, they found it far too expensive and had to use thistledown instead. All the goblins made new suits for themselves out of the finest bat-fur; the demons polished their asbestos coats; and the only people who didn't have fun were the ghosts and will-o'-the-wisps, whose clothes—if you could call them clothes—were made of nothing but fog and vapour, which was one reason why their owners were unpopular. You couldn't be very friendly with a person who turned into a puddle right before your eyes; it even made the demons uncomfortable, and *they* were pretty hard-boiled, as we say in our day.

The Seven Witches worked harder than anyone else. All day long the spinning-wheels clattered and hummed, and from the distaff streamed yards and yards of glittering coal-dust. As fast as they spun it they cut it up into dress-lengths, and then *snip, snip* went their scissors, trimming and shaping and clipping, and *flash, zip, whing* went the needles, till *Abracadabra!*—the gowns were finished, and the morning of the ball had arrived.

It was a day of glorious sunshine. The whole countryside had put on its best dress in honour of the occasion. The choke-cherries and dogwoods were wearing their cream lace; the forests had put on all their jewels, hepaticas in jasper and amethyst, golden adder's tongue, silver sweet violets, and through the deepest, darkest woods you could see the glimmer of pearl-white bloodroot, each flower the shape of a star. Every tree wore a new spring hat of palest green; even the swamps had smartened themselves up and carried bouquets of blue flags and bulrushes.

The Seven Witches got up very early and went out to the barn to see the Horse. He had been fed all week on the finest oats and rye-straw. Curiously enough he did not take to this diet very well, and neighed and stamped his feet when it was brought to him, refusing to touch it for hours, until he grew terribly hungry and had to nibble a little of it, finally gulping it all down and then looking very miserable, drooping his knees and hanging his silver mane down to the floor, until the witches got frightened, seeing their grand appearance at the ball fading away from them.

So this morning they brought a bowl of milk-porridge and a dish of maple sugar and gave them to the Horse. He gobbled at it greedily, and while he was eating they stroked him and brushed him and spoke nicely to him, so that the poor thing brightened up wonderfully, and began to arch his neck again and toss his shining head quite proudly.

"Take him out," said Trouble to Scowl, "and ride him up and down gently. Don't speak sharply to him, and don't dig your toes into his ribs; he must be in a good mood for tonight."

Scowl wasn't very good at being gentle, for she was a sour-faced cross-grained old woman; she had a long nose like a snout and little piggy eyes that glittered in the dark. However, she knew when to do what she was told; so she led the Horse out, got on his back and rode him quietly along the path that went down to the lake, keeping her toes well stuck out at the sides so that she wouldn't be tempted to kick the Horse in the ribs.

Now it happened that this morning Doctor Troyer's son Michael had got up early and come out along the cliffs. Michael was upset about the loss of his father, who had disappeared without anyone seeing him go or knowing what had become of him, and he wanted to be alone to think everything out carefully. He was a handsome young man, tall and slender, with clever hands and bright clear eyes like a deer's. He came along slowly, his eyes fixed on the ground, because he could think better that way; so he did not see Scowl and the Horse till they were almost upon him. Indeed he didn't see Scowl at all, for only bad-minded people see bad things, and Michael was a good boy and thought well of everybody. So it was all the more surprising to him when he looked up and saw the Horse's silver mane towering above him, and the wide pink nostrils spread and quivering like rose-petals in the wind. Michael was not at all afraid, for animals were always kind to him; so he put his hand on the Horse's soft nose and said mildly:

"Poor old fellow!"

Then a queer thing happened. The Horse opened his mouth and spoke.

"Michael! Michael!"

Scowl, who was annoyed at meeting Michael and angry with herself for having forgotten to magic the Horse so that he would be invisible, pulled out a hickory switch and gave the Horse a sharp cut across the flanks. He plunged and reared, and she struck him again; but before they galloped away the Horse once more cried out pitifully:

"Michael! Michael!"

You can imagine how Michael felt. He didn't know why the Horse had plunged and run away so fast; but he saw great tears in the creature's eyes, and knew that something dreadful must have happened. For some reason that he did not understand he thought of his father, and he determined to follow the strange white Horse and see what it was all about.

Scowl took the Horse back to the barn as fast as he could go, and not a word did she say to her sisters about meeting Michael on the cliffs. All the rest of the day the witches bustled about, getting out their best undies and putting

180

finishing touches to the new gowns. They brushed their scraggy hair and scrubbed their ugly faces, and then looked in their mirrors and admired themselves—which was a good thing, because certainly no one else would.

At last it was time to start for the ball, and you could hear the flurry of excitement all across Long Point. Bats scurried past with pixies and goblins on their backs; rats and mice, put under a charm for the night, dragged little carts for the sprites, who were small and hadn't a chance of getting a bat or a hawk to ride on; demons flew along with red-hot sparks stolen from the blacksmith's forge tied to their tails. It was all very festive and exciting. The four winds had come out to watch the fun, and were roaring through the tree-tops, blowing dust over everyone and generally making mischief.

At Dunkirk the whole sky was lighted with huge bon-fires, each one leaping as high as the moon and sizzling with sulphur and brimstone. Across the lake a great search-light made a path for the arriving guests; the waves crashed underneath and the winds screamed overhead, but the Powers of Darkness had spread Black Magic all over the night, and no one could touch the revellers or stop their evil laughter.

Everyone had arrived and people were wondering why the party did not begin, when someone said:

"Where are the Seven Witches? We can't begin without them!"

Just then a tremendous clapping and shouting arose from the guests nearest the lake-shore, and everyone turned to see what was happening. Then *they* began to clap too, until the whole assembly was cheering and applauding. This was what they saw.

Down the long crimson path of the searchlight the White Horse stepped slowly. His mane gleamed like a thousand diamonds; his eyes flashed in the hot red light until they looked like live coals; his harness was made of precious stones, and his hoofs were painted pure gold. On his back, dressed in their new-spun finery, sat the Seven Witches, Trouble, Rags, Tatters, Scowl, Wrinkle, Miss (who was the least old and ugly), and little Hit hanging on over the Horse's tail. Their cloaks floating in the wind made banners over their heads, and every time the Horse took a step their earrings rang like brass trumpets. It was a wonderful entrance, and even the witches' vanity must have been satisfied as they rode into the shouting crowd of guests, who swarmed round them and fought for the honour of helping them to alight.

Soon the ball was in full swing. Black grasshoppers fiddled for the dances, ghostly drummers beat unseen drums; through the scarlet glow of the bonfires the dancers whirled and twisted like dry leaves in a furnace. The witches were in great demand; in fact the moment they entered the ball-room the Personage from Detroit, as gorgeously arrayed as ever, presented himself with a low bow and begged the honour of opening the dance with Madame Trouble. How graciously Trouble accepted, and how proudly her sisters watched as she sailed down the ballroom on the Personage's arm!

Meanwhile the Horse had been tied up in an old barn near by, with only a handful of rye-straw that Scowl had tossed in as she left him. He was thirsty after his run through the hot lights, and his jewelled harness scratched him horribly; he moaned a little to himself, and sometimes he murmured under his breath:

"Michael! Michael!"

Then the four winds would blow mournfully, as though they tried to answer him; but it didn't make him feel any better.

Presently, however, as he stood sighing and puffing through his nostrils, he thought he heard another sound echoing him. He pricked up his ears and listened sharply. Yes, there *was* something—a soft *sst! sst!* like the sound you make when you want someone to listen. Then came a gentle tapping on the side of the barn: tap, tap, tap-a-tap *tap*; tap, tap, tap-a-tap *tap*. When the Horse heard it he flew into a terrific state of excitement. He couldn't neigh or whinny for fear of someone at the Ball hearing and coming to see what was the matter; but he tossed his head up and down till the jewels on his headpiece rang against each other and made this tune: ting, ting, ting-a-tang *ting*. Then the taps answered:

"Tap-tap. Tap-tap. Tap-a-tap-a-tap *tap*."

Of course it was Michael who was tapping outside the barn. He had followed Scowl home, had hidden outside the witches' window and heard something that made his hair curl as tight as a little pig's tail. Trouble had spoken his father's name, and then the witches had laughed till cold chills ran up and down Michael's backbone; they had wagged their heads and said:

"Ah-ha! We'll give the old man a run for his money!"

Now Michael was very good at putting two and two together; you may make it add up to four, but in Magic, everyone knows, it always makes five. Therefore he realized at once that his father's disappearance and the witches' unkind laughter had something to do with each other, and he set to work to find out what it was. Through a crack in the door he watched the preparations for the ball, being careful to skip away and hide in the bushes whenever the witches came out. He saw the Horse led out and dressed in his costly harness; he hid behind the barn while the witches mounted and set out on their journey. Being a good runner he was able to follow them—at a safe distance of course— until they came to the lake; then he didn't know what to do. It was too rough to swim even if he could have kept up with the Horse, who was being Magicked through the air; so he stood very miserably on the shore, wondering what to do next. As he wondered he put his hands in his pockets, and suddenly he felt a little hard thing between his fingers. His father's moonstone! They had been out walking one day and the Doctor, hunting for herbs, had given the moonstone to Michael; he had slipped it into his pocket, and there it had been ever since.

Luckily he knew what to do with the stone, although he had been told never to use it unless the occasion was very urgent. Surely this was urgent, he thought; so he lifted the

184

moonstone in his right hand, turned himself round three times, and recited:

Stone, stone, moonstone, wake;
Carry me over the stormy lake.

Then he held out his arms, and *whoosh!*—up to the clouds he rose, and over the lake so fast that people who saw him thought he was a shooting star. He was a bit breathless when he was put down on the other side, not being used to travelling so quickly; but he put the moonstone in his pocket and looked about to see what had become of the Horse and the witches. He heard the music from the ballroom, and saw the whirling figures; very quietly he crept round the dance-hall and found the old barn at the back. There he heard the Horse moaning to himself, and tapped as I have told you.

Now the question was, what was to be done? The barn door was locked, and he didn't know anything about opening locked doors. He wished that he had taken the trouble to learn more Magic from his father, who would never let a little thing like a locked door stand in his way. While he stood thinking, a little screech-owl flew close to him.

"Michael," it said, "Michael."

Michael understood screech-owls, so he held up his finger for it to sit on, and it hooted gently in his ear:

"Try the roof! Try the roof!"

Michael had no idea what it meant, but he was ready to do anything; so he ran round the barn, and there at the

185

side was a ladder. Up it he went, and on to the roof he crawled. There, close to the eaves, was a little hole, and with a good deal of pushing and scrambling he got through, crept along the beams that supported the roof, and climbed down into the mow. Soon he was standing beside the Horse, who had been watching him in trembling excitement, and who now began to nose at the pocket where the moonstone was. Michael took the stone out and held it on the palm of his hand, wondering what to do next, when to his alarm the Horse calmly picked up the stone in his teeth and swallowed it.

"Good gracious!" said Michael, and then he said, "Good gracious," again, very loud, for suddenly the whole barn began to rock and sway as though an earthquake were going on. Everything went dark, too, and in the blackness things rushed and flapped, there were squeakings and hootings as if giant bats and owls were beating the air. Then the whole turmoil was hushed, light came again, and there beside Michael stood his father, smiling his usual kindly smile, the moonstone in his hand.

"The Horse!" cried Michael; but the Horse had vanished.

"I was the Horse," said the Doctor. "Dear me, hadn't you discovered that?" He took his son by the arm and walked him out of the barn; the door had unlocked itself, apparently, for it was swinging wide open.

"You see," remarked the Doctor, "there are times when a little bit of Magic is very useful. If you had memorized the Six Good Rules when I wanted you to, you would have

186

known exactly what to do when I disappeared. As it was, you were almost too late."

"Too late?" asked Michael anxiously.

"Yes. If you hadn't found me before midnight I should have been in the hands of the Powers of Darkness forever. So it was a good thing you remembered as much as you did, eh?"

"Yes, Father," said Michael, and he hung his head and looked so downcast that his father, who thought him a wonderful boy but never let him guess it, patted his arm and said kindly:

"It was clever of you to have thought of the tap signals. I should never have known you were there if you hadn't."

By this time they had come to the lake-shore, and the Doctor said:

"Shall we play a little joke on the party before we go home?" He picked up a handful of sand and threw it over his left shoulder, murmuring a Magic as he did so. Then he held up the moonstone, and in the flick of a cat's whisker he and Michael were safely at home, sitting in front of a blazing fire of birch logs with Eileen bringing them hot possets of honey and lemon juice.

But something had happened to the ball at Dunkirk. At the very moment the Doctor threw the sand over his left shoulder every dancer in the ballroom began to cry. They didn't know why they were doing it, but they cried and cried and couldn't stop at all. They sobbed and sniffled and choked and wheezed; they leaned on one another's shoulders and the tears poured down their new clothes and

187

washed all the wax off the ballroom floor. They used up all their clean handkerchiefs and had to begin using the window-curtains; they tried cold water, hot water, ice on the head, poultices on the feet, all of no use. At last the whole party broke up, because it is no fun being at a party when your eyes are so red and swollen you can't see anything.

Everyone crept away very quietly, and there were the tables loaded with wonderful food which no one had felt like eating. Then all the little birds and beasts who had been watching the party through the windows came trooping in, and they sat down in the best places and gobbled and gobbled until every scrap of food and every drop of drink had disappeared. Most of them were sick the next day, but they didn't mind because none of them had ever had such a grand feast before.

Now the witches were very angry, as you can imagine, when they found the barn door wide open and the Horse gone. They were so miserable with their streaming eyes and sore noses that they would gladly have ridden off on their old broomsticks if the broomsticks hadn't been thrown away and burnt on the rubbish-heap. There was nothing to do but set out on foot, which they did; and when they came to the lake they had to swim, and the water washed off their coal-dust gowns, and their eyes smarted and their heads ached, and by the time they got home at last they were as unhappy a crew as you could wish to see.

"I shall apply for a transfer to another district," croaked Trouble as she staggered off to bed. "I shall refuse to live in this place another moonrise."

188

"We all refuse," cried the other witches; but by morning they all had double-pneumonia and would have died if they had been humans. Instead they were left with rheumatism and gout and arthritis and sciatica, and were no use to anybody, so they were given the Witches' Old-Age Pension and sent off to knit snow-suits for the pixies.

And from that day forward the Powers of Darkness left Long Point severely alone, and a lot of good people were able to come and live there in peace and security.

But it was said that Doctor Troyer suffered from indigestion for many years afterwards, on account of the rye-straw fed to him by the witches.

The Story of Good Saint Anne

This is a story to be read when you are going to bed at night, or leaving home for the first time, or when you are tired and frightened and the world seems a cold place.

For Saint Anne is the saint of all travellers, and poor people, and little children; she is the guardian of those who work with their hands and live by their own labours; she is kind and loving, never refusing help to anyone who asks— at least this is what the *habitants* of French Canada believe, so it won't do us any harm to believe it too.

191

All through the Province of Quebec there are little way-side shrines dedicated to Saint Anne. Chapels are built for her in great cathedrals; towns and villages and many parish churches are named for her. There are pictures of her, too —pink and white and gold, with smooth hair and gracious, pointed hands, like the saints in old paintings. *Bonne Sainte Anne*, the French children call her; and because she is so much loved and held in honour, I will tell you a story about her and the miracles done in her name.

Past the ancient city of Quebec that wears the Citadel like a king's crown upon its head, lies the gentle valley of the St. Charles River, where long ago Jacques Cartier and his men built their flimsy shelters against the bitter Canadian winter. Across the St. Charles you are out in a mild countryside full of little farms and whitewashed barns lying placidly along the banks of the River St. Lawrence as it goes climbing, climbing northwards to the sea. This bit of land is called the Côte de Beaupré, and at certain times of the year all kinds of people are to be seen going along its roads toward the little village of Saint Anne de Beaupré. There will be farmers and their families, friars in black robes and brown, townsfolk in their shining cars, and Indians in canoes or sleighs pushing their way up the river to sell baskets, ornaments, and beaded moccasins to the white pilgrims.

For Saint Anne de Beaupré, they say, is a place where miracles happen: blind people see, the lame are healed, the deaf hear—at least the pilgrims who go there believe so.

And it is all because of something that began so long ago that it is difficult to count the years.

Saint Anne was the mother of Mary, who was the mother of Jesus. She was a wise and gentle person, and when she died her friends and relatives mourned deeply, and they buried her under the olive trees on a quiet hillside in Jerusalem. Here her body rested peacefully until troubled times came and Palestine was overrun by Mohammedan soldiers who tore down Christian churches and did all the damage they could. They destroyed the tomb of the good Saint Anne; but although they tried hard they could neither burn nor tear open her coffin. So they threw it into the sea; and instead of sinking to the bottom, it floated gently on the waves of the Mediterranean until it came to the shores of France, where it was pushed up on the beach; and the tides washed the soft white sand over it, deeper and deeper, until it was quite buried.

Many years passed, and one day some fisher lads were playing in the sand, digging moats and building castles.

"I'll dig a deeper hole than you will," cried one.

The other said: "I'm stronger than you. *My* hole will be deepest."

And they dug and dug, each determined to outdo the other. Suddenly one cried:

"I've found buried treasure!"

His friend rushed to look. Sure enough, there was a long box bound at the corners with metal and having strange carvings upon it. The boys dug with their spades

193

and managed to drag it out. It was heavy, but there was no lock upon it and so they did not know how to open it.

"We will take it home," they said to one another. "Our father will know what to do."

So they carried it home, holding it on their shoulders, and when their father saw it he said:

"This is not for us to meddle with. We will take it to the priest."

Now the priest was good Bishop Aurelius. When the casket was brought to him he blessed it and prayed over it, and when he touched the lid it opened, and the body of Saint Anne was inside. Then the Bishop was amazed, and knelt very humbly to give thanks to God. And because the times were rough and dangerous, they did not put the casket in the church, but built a strong wall, and inside the wall a crypt or tomb; and here the casket was placed, and the wall sealed up so that none should know what was in it.

For many more years the casket rested safely, until the Emperor Charlemagne had the wall taken down, and there was the coffin inside. After that it was taken from place to place, until it was laid in a shrine at a little town in Brittany where the French people came to worship and to say their prayers to Saint Anne.

And there it would have been to this day if it had not been for a certain man who lived near the shrine, and who used to watch the townsfolk going to and fro with their candles and their rosaries. This man was a discontented, brooding sort of fellow, who dreamed of doing some marvellous deed for which his name would become famous.

194

One day an idea came to him, and he stole into the shrine, took the sacred casket, and carried it aboard a ship bound for America. It would be a wonderful thing, he thought, if he could show the casket in some far-off place, and boast that it contained the bones of Saint Anne. People would flock to him, and he would be wealthy and important.

But his greed did not do him much good, for the voyage was rough, and he fell overboard and was drowned in the Atlantic; and for all his loud talk Saint Anne could not save him.

Yet in the end good came out of it, for the sailors aboard the vessel knew what was in the casket. It would be a shame, said they, to send poor Saint Anne all the way back to France after such buffeting and tossing on the ocean; so they took a vow to build a shrine for her at the first spot where they touched land, and that spot was the Côte de Beaupré. They built a tiny wooden chapel, and placed the casket of Saint Anne on the altar; and that was the first Church of Saint Anne de Beaupré.

Many a sailor knelt at the shrine to give thanks for a safe voyage over the stormy Atlantic, and many a brave priest brought his Indian converts there to take their first Sacrament. Then, in the terrible warfare with the Iroquois, the whole village was wrecked and burned except the little church, which stood untouched by the Indians' flaming torches, so that they went away from it saying that the place was bewitched. At last the wood of the chapel began to rot, and it was no longer safe for people to worship there; so a fine new building was laid out, and all the *habitants* took turns to dig the foundations and lay the stones. And now a strange thing happened.

There lived in Beaupré a man whose name was Louis Guimont. He was a good man, and he and his family burned many a candle to Saint Anne, for it was she, they said, who had brought them to this rich land and made their farm prosper. But Louis had been through many hardships, and the long cold winters without proper shelter had stiffened his limbs, so that they were racked with rheumatism and sometimes he could scarcely walk.

"Henriette," he said to his wife, "you must help me down to the shore where they are building the new church. I must lay at least one stone with my own hands."

His wife tried to reason with him.

"Eh, Louis, how could a cripple like you lift heavy stones? Saint Anne would not expect it. Stay at home and rest."

But Louis was determined.

"Help me down," said he, "for I cannot tell another rosary until I have laid the stone."

So Henriette wrapped him in his sheepskin coat and tied his muffler about his neck; and then slowly, with painful and faltering steps, Louis made his way to the spot where the new church was being built.

The other workers cheered when they saw him, for Louis was loved by everybody. There were plenty of willing hands ready to lift the stone for him so that he might ease it into place; but he would have no help, and they had to stand by, helpless, while with great pain and

196

difficulty he stooped, got his hands about the great stone and tried to lift it towards its place in the wall. In vain! He could not move it, and the kind neighbours rushed forward to support him. But he waved them back and stooped again to the stone.

Then the watchers saw the miracle. Suddenly, as Louis bent his tortured back, his face lost its lines of pain and an expression of joy and amazement spread over it.

"I can do it!" he cried, and with that he swept the stone up as though it had been a handful of sand, carried it to the wall, and set it, not on the low place they had left for it, but high above his head on the next ridge of the structure. As the onlookers gasped for astonishment, he turned to them, standing straight and strong, and cried in a loud voice:

"Praise the good God! I am healed!"

Then all the people knelt down where they were and gave thanks. From that day Louis Guimont had no more pain; and that was the first miracle of Saint Anne.

Now in this day of our Lord in which we live, pilgrims still flock to the shrine of Saint Anne at Beaupré and seek healing for their ills. Perhaps the gentle Saint Anne watches over their prayers. Who shall say? You will see the crutches piled in the porch of the church, left there, we are told, by thankful sufferers who have no more need of them. From all across Canada they come, and if they have faith they are healed.

The Lament of Cadieux

If you live in French Canada, you will have learned when you were very small to sing the *chansons* taught by the *habitants* to their children round the fire on winter evenings. You will remember some songs better than others, and will never forget, once you have heard it, the gentle rocking melody known as the Song of Cadieux. Sometimes the French people call it *Le Petit Rocher*—"The Little Rock". The story I'm going to tell explains the song, and if you have heard it before you won't mind hearing it again, because it is that kind of a story.

First you had better hum the melody of the song, through (softly, to yourself). If you don't know it, ask someone else to sing it to you; and if they don't know it, it is time they learned. For this is one of the sweetest, saddest, and oldest songs of French Canada, and it was first sung, perhaps, far back in history when Sieur de Champlain sailed the blue St. Lawrence and built his *Habitation* on the rocks of Quebec.

This is the story.

Everyone knows about the *coureurs-de-bois,* those brave trappers and hunters who went up and down the country in their canoes or on foot, making their living dangerously and fearing no man. In the early days of the white men in Canada, one of these hunters was named Antoine Cadieux. His name might not have been Antoine, for in the years that have passed his Christian name has been somehow forgotten; but he must have had one, and Antoine is a good name. This Cadieux was a man who loved adventure. Even the roving life of the *coureur-de-bois* did not quite content him, so he went farther afield than his fellows, pushing his canoe up strange waters and deep into the northern wilderness where only the Indian inhabitants knew the trails. There was always danger of getting caught by the terrible Iroquois, whom all the world feared; but Cadieux trusted *le bon Dieu,* and came back from his journeys unhurt and still unafraid.

One of these journeys took him up the great River Ottawa, over long portages and through swift currents. He and his Indian guides camped for the night on the shores of a little inlet, between the Islands Allumette and Calumet. Here they met an Algonquin chief who lived with his family near the river. This chief had been visited by the Recollet friars from Quebec, and he and his wife and children had been baptized and taught to live as white men lived.

Now the chief had a daughter, young and very beautiful. She had learned all that the priests could teach her, and she longed to travel and see for herself some of the scenes and people they described to her. They told her of their native France, of Paris with its wonderful streets and fair buildings; and she, who had never set foot beyond the shores of the Ottawa and the forests surrounding her father's home, yearned, like the princesses in old fairy tales, for a handsome lover who would take her away to far countries.

You may imagine what happened when the Lily of the Ottawa met the young hunter, Antoine Cadieux. For Cadieux was big and broad and good to look at, with black hair curling to his shoulders and eyes that flashed and laughed like the waters of the Seven Chutes tumbling over the rocks near Calumet. Cadieux had never seen an Indian girl like this one. She would sit for hours with her chin in her hand, listening to the stories he told her: tales of peril and adventure, of long journeys under the stars and strange encounters with man and beast. Any man will love a lady who gladly hears him talk; and so, before many moons had passed, Cadieux and the dusky Lily were to be married, and

201

the Algonquin father was happy. Now, he said, the longing of her heart will be satisfied.

And for a time it was so. Cadieux and his wife made their home near her father's settlement. They built a cabin of birch and pine, and from their windows they could see the silver waters of the river and hear the soft rush of the rapids below. Cadieux took shorter journeys now so that he could hurry home to the little house where the Lily waited for him; but he never took her with him or suggested that they go exploring together as they had planned before they were married.

Then a boy and a girl came to the Cadieux cabin, and Antoine hurried home even faster, eager to see his son and daughter. But yet the Lily waited for him to take her on the journeys her heart longed for, even while she rocked the baby Lily in her birch-bark cradle or skipped pebbles on the shore with Pierre, who talked of the time when he would grow up and go voyaging with his father.

At last one day, when Cadieux was getting his furs ready to take to the trading-post, the Lily said:

"Antoine, take me with you to the Lake of the Two Mountains. It is not very far—even my brothers go there to barter furs. I will take the children home to our mother, and we will journey together."

Cadieux took her hand in his and said:

"What could this small hand do if a storm came and the canoe was foundering?"

The Lily answered: "It could paddle right stoutly, and

if the canoe overturned it could swim until shelter was reached."

Then Cadieux said: "If savage tribes attacked us, what could this small hand do?"

And the Lily replied: "It could throw a hatchet and string an arrow as swiftly as thou, my husband."

Cadieux kissed his Algonquin and said:

"You shall go with me, clever one, to the Lake of the Two Mountains; but before we go we will pray to the good Saint Anne that no harm may come to you."

For no Frenchman thought of going on a journey without asking for Saint Anne's protection, and all through Quebec they built shrines in her honour, each with its little halo of candles lit by those who prayed.

So Cadieux and his wife did what they had always done on the eve of Antoine's voyages. They went together to their own small shrine in the woods, lit their candles, and said their prayers. Cadieux's prayer was for the Lily, but hers was for him and for the children.

The next morning they set off early in their canoe while the mists still hung above the river and the first glimmer of sun slanted across the hills. It was the fall of the year when the Saint Lawrence country wears its most beautiful dress. The crests of the mountains were pale blue, their rounded sides a riot of colour—rose, crimson, scarlet, copper, with here and there a scarf of brilliant green where birches or willows had not yet turned their leaves into gold. The river ran smoothly, like moving glass, for there was no wind; water dripped in silver strings from the paddles. The

Lily's hair was frosted with mist; she laughed as she swung her paddle. At last she was a *voyageur*, going out to see the world. Cadieux laughed with her, glad because of her happiness.

At the portage of the Seven Chutes they were to meet a party of Algonquins, also going to Mount Royal. Cadieux landed the canoe in sight of the rapids; beautiful they looked, but very treacherous, hiding their sharp-headed rocks under a whirl of froth and rainbow spray. The Indians were waiting, squatting on the shore. Behind them rose the blue Laurentian mountains; sumac blazed on the hillsides as though someone had lighted a trail of fires. The Lily was enchanted; she ran here and there, gathering bitter-sweet to tie in her hair. Cadieux did not hurry her; they had made an early start and the sun was still low in the east, so he lay watching her and skipping little stones into the water, as Pierre did on the shore at home.

Suddenly footsteps crackled at the edge of the woods. A young Indian ran swiftly towards them, making signs with his hands as he came. The Algonquins leaped to their feet, grasping guns and tomahawks; among them ran a murmur like a rush of wind:

"Iroquois!"

Cadieux caught the messenger, asked him rapid questions. The boy was breathless and terrified.

"In the woods—many men—coming this way!"

As he spoke the Indians, heading for the canoes, raised a howl of fright. Down the smooth river pathway they had just travelled came a fleet of war-canoes; the brown arms of the Iroquois could be seen flashing in the sunlight as they plied the paddles. Retreat by water was cut off; the woods were swarming with red men yelling war-cries.

Like frightened rabbits the Algonquins would have run for the shelter of the trees where they would have been easily surrounded, but Cadieux acted swiftly.

"Into the canoes!" he shouted to the Indians, and swept up the Lily as though she were a pinch of thistledown. The men, too terrified to think for themselves, obeyed blindly; their canoes shot out from the shore and headed for the rapids. Cadieux put the Lily into their own canoe and thrust the paddle into her hands.

"Paddle!" he cried, and pushed the canoe into the water.

The Lily was out on the current before she knew that her husband was not with her.

"Antoine!" She stood up, the little craft rocking beneath her. Cadieux shouted from the shore:

"Paddle for the rapids! Don't be afraid! I'll be with you—later!"

The Lily hesitated, wanting to leap overboard and swim back. Then the canoe bounced against a rock and she was flung down, still clutching at the paddle. She heard Cadieux's voice shouting:

"Paddle! Paddle!"

Instinctively she struggled to right the canoe, which was being thrown up and down like a cork on the turbulent water; the Lily had sailed in rough weather before, and she knew what to do. Yet as she paddled desperately she saw the foam of the rapids ahead and shut her eyes, expecting to be hurled against the cruel edges of the rocks. Cadieux's voice rang in her ears above the drumming of the water:

"Paddle! And Saint Anne defend you!"

From the shore Cadieux saw the little boat disappear. Someone touched him on the arm; he turned and saw the young messenger.

"Why didn't you go with the others?" demanded Cadieux.

"I stay to help you," said the boy.

Cadieux caught his shoulder. "Then do as I tell you. The Iroquois will try to overtake our canoes; we must stop them. Have you got a gun?"

The lad showed his weapon.

"Into the woods with me, then."

They ran for the woods as the leading canoes swept down the shore-line.

"Turn right and shoot off your gun," shouted Cadieux to the boy, "then double back and make for the cabin. I'll join you as soon as I can. We must make them think there are a great number of us."

They reached the woods; yells from the Iroquois showed that they had been seen.

"Shoot," muttered Cadieux, and they discharged their guns. The reports rang out loudly; the echoes, flying back, sounded like other guns answering them. Cadieux nodded to the lad and waved him on.

"Heaven keep you," he cried, as they plunged into the dark bushes, Cadieux towards the island, the Indian boy in

206

the opposite direction. The branches crashed and shook, then there was silence, until like a dark cloud the Iroquois broke from their canoes and streamed into the woods, the air hideous with their war-cries.

What happened after that is told by the Lily and the Algonquins who went before her on that perilous journey. As I have said, when she saw the waters of the whirlpool rise up before her she gave herself into the care of the holy saints; she prayed, and her prayers were for Antoine, left in the grip of the terrible enemy. She paddled no more; but suddenly she heard the roar of the rapids round her, and still the canoe rode onward. She opened her eyes. White spray rose in clouds, almost blinding her; but through the stinging vapour she saw, poised like the angels in her pictures at home, the figure of a tall woman whose draperies floated on the mist like a golden halo. She bent towards the Lily, and her outspread hands seemed to beckon.

"It was the good Saint Anne, sent from Heaven to guide me," said the Lily afterwards to the traders who took her, wet and exhausted, but unhurt, to the shelter of the trading-post at the foot of the Lake of Two Mountains. The Algonquins who had gone ahead of her were safe too, for they had followed her canoe when it shot past them in the rapids, and it had led them through a channel in the rocks and out into the calm water of the lake.

But what had happened to Cadieux? It was many days before anyone knew, for although search-parties went out from Mount Royal and spent long hours tramping the forests, they found no trace of him. It was the Lily who found him at last, and the story that has made its way down three centuries was told for the first time.

The Iroquois, puzzled by the sound of guns and yet seeing no enemies, scattered through the woods searching for them. The Indian lad, running in a circle as Cadieux had told him to do, fell into the hands of the savages and died bravely, defending himself and committing his spirit to God. Cadieux, knowing the forests as one knows the pages of a favourite book, hid himself until the Iroquois grew tired of looking for him and camped for the night. The next morning he tried to slip past their sentries, but they saw him and followed, yelling to awaken the rest of the encampment. Cadieux closed with his pursuers, killed two of them and escaped; but he had been wounded in the shoulder, and although he ran as well as he could, he knew he could never reach home.

Near the portage there was a little cave in the rocks. Cadieux crept in and pulled branches and leaves over the entrance to deceive the Indians if they should pass by. He was very weak, from hunger and his wound; for a time he tried to crawl out and look for berries and roots, but it was too much for him. Once he even heard voices quite near at hand. With all his might he shouted, but the sound he made was so tiny and faint that the friends who were looking for him passed within a few yards of his shelter and heard nothing. After that Cadieux knew that he was to die, and having done all that he could, his mind was at rest.

Lying on his bed of leaves and pine-needles, looking out at the blue sky, he thought about the Lily and his heart ached for her sorrow. If she lives, he thought, she will find me. But by then I shall be gone; only my body will be here to distress her. Then, looking up, he saw above his shelter the bending branches of a silver birch tree. "I will write my story on the bark of this tree," he said, "a song for my son to remember. And they will know that I died in peace."

With the sharp end of a broken twig he wrote on the soft, fresh surface of the birch-bark. It took him several days, for he was very weak. It was finished at twilight, when the warm glow of the sun faded behind the pine-trees. It was very still in the forest, and a few late golden leaves drifted down on the little shelter. Cadieux lay back on his sweet-scented bed, folded his hands on his breast, and breathed a prayer to *le bon Dieu* who had saved him from his enemies.

When the sun came up again in the morning, the soul of Antoine had gone aloft to the saints.

So the Lily found him, lying peacefully, a smile on his face, his hands clasped over the message he had written for her. They buried him near the portage where he gave his life for the people he loved. If you pass along the Ottawa River you may think of him there, and say a prayer in his memory. The tale written on the birch-bark was told in hushed tones round many a *habitant* table, over many a camp-fire. The *voyageurs* told it to one another on their journeys, so that it took on the slow swinging rhythm of the paddles, and at last it was set to the plaintive melody we know.

Petit rocher de la haute montagne,
Je viens ici finir cette campagne,
Ah! doux échos, entendez mes soupirs,
En languissant je vais bientôt mourir.

The Devil and the Wind

Once upon a time, in the city of Montreal, the Devil and the Wind were out walking. It was a dullish sort of day, the kind when the sky and the earth and the water all look the same colour, and people go about with pinched noses and red eyes. The ladies were having difficulty with their skirts; for in those days skirts were very different from the ones worn now—there were a great many of them, all full and frilly, and they bounced along on the ground and got wet and dirty and gave their owners no end of trouble.

The Wind knew this very well; so every time he saw a

group of ladies coming along he blew out his cheeks, and whoof! up went the skirts, and the ladies gave little genteel cries (for in those days everyone was genteel) and did their best to smooth them down again, which wasn't easy, because there was a great deal too much skirt to be managed by one pair of little gloved hands. Then the Wind would roar with laughter, and the ladies would scuttle past quickly in case he should blow again.

"I don't see," said the Devil peevishly after one of these incidents, "what there is to be so gay about. I find the day extremely depressing."

"Depressing?" cried the Wind. "With so many amusing people about?"

"They bore me," said the Devil. "Everybody bores me."

"Dear me," remarked the Wind, doing a hop, skip, and jump to keep up with the Devil, who was walking very fast, "you must be very tired indeed to find life so uninteresting. I must try and brighten you up a bit. Watch me and I'll give you a good laugh."

With that he bounded across the street, got behind an old gentleman who was out for a stroll with his dog and his umbrella, and began pushing him along at such a pace that the old fellow's legs could hardly trot fast enough. He clutched at his hat, dropped his umbrella, and went sailing down the street, helter skelter, clippity-clop, with the Wind swooping behind him and the little dog shrieking at his heels. They were running full tilt down Beaver Hall Hill; if you've ever been there you know how steep it is. Faster and faster went the little old gentleman, and as he reached the bottom of the hill where the road takes a twist into Victoria Square, he went crack into a lamp post. He was going too quickly to stop, so up the post he shot, and there he hung at the top, his coat-tails flapping like ducks' wings and the little dog screaming below.

The Wind, who had stopped half way down the hill, waited, doubled up with laughter, for the Devil to catch up with him—which he did presently, walking fast and looking very cross.

"Wasn't that fun? Don't you feel better?" shouted the Wind.

"I wasn't amused," said the Devil coldly, not knowing that he was saying almost the very words that would be used one day by a famous queen and remembered by all the world.

"Well," said the Wind, "you *are* an ungrateful fellow. Let's go a little further; something exciting is bound to turn up."

They walked on till they came to Notre Dame Street, and here the Wind gave a whoop of joy.

"We're in luck, my dear," he cried to the Devil. "Here are some of my friends from the country. Now you'll be royally entertained."

The Devil saw in front of him a party of *habitants* on their way to the big Market a little distance away. There were farmers in bright-coloured shirts, their wives with gay kerchiefs round their heads, and children trundling hoops or playing with woollen balls. Some of the men pushed

213

carts filled with wares for the market—apples and pears and potatoes, carrots, cabbages, eggs, fine fat chickens, and ducks—a goodly sight to see.

The Wind, chuckling to himself, pranced to meet them. First he hummed gently round the carts, lifting the cloths that covered the poultry and rattling the apples in their baskets; then he got a little rougher, pushed over a few cabbages, snatched a cap from a man's head, and blew the hoop out of a little boy's hand. The child began to cry, and with that the Wind opened up his bag of tricks and showed what he could do.

He tore the carts away from their owners and sent them rushing along the street by themselves, bumpity-bump over the cobblestones; he flung the fruit and vegetables here and there, and tossed the poultry over the roof-tops; a fine brace of ducks landed in the garden of St. Sulpice Seminary and was picked up by one of the friars who hurried indoors with it without looking too hard to see where it came from—for the good fathers did not often have the chance of roast duck for their supper.

The farmers ran after their possessions as well as they could; but as fast as they picked things up the Wind snatched them away again, until from Notre Dame to the river-front the ground was littered with hats, caps, hoops, baskets, poultry, fruit, vegetables, and other bits and pieces, not to mention the eggs, which all rolled together down Saint Gabriel hill and landed *smash!* into a fishmarket, where the fishmonger's wife scooped them up and made a grand omelette—and like the friar *she* didn't bother about where they came from.

So everybody was happy except the *habitants*, who had only empty carts to take to the market; and the little old gentleman, still hanging from the lamp-post; and the Devil, who sat coldly on the street corner with his tail curled round his feet like a cat's.

The Wind, meanwhile, having done all the mischief he could think of, went bouncing back to the Devil, trumpeting as he came:

"Wasn't that magnificent? Did you ever see a better show in your life?"

The Devil flicked his eyebrows, twitched his horns, and answered calmly:

"I am not amused yet."

The Wind cut a caper, turned two somersaults, did a *fouetté* and a couple of *entrechâts* (any dancing-teacher will do them for you), and landed on all fours in front of the Devil.

"Man, you're not human!" he shouted; then burst into one of his great laughs. "Of course you're not human! You're the Devil!"

His majesty got up, looking dignified.

"If you can't find anything better to do than to sit there laughing, I think we will part company. It isn't becoming for me to be about with such a person."

He began to walk away. The Wind leaped up and caught his coat-tails.

"Wait a second," said he. "Don't be so hasty. I can be as quiet as anybody when I choose."

So they went along together, the Wind being quiet and the Devil not saying anything; and presently they came to the corner of Saint Sulpice Street where it wanders across Notre Dame on its way to the river.

"Sulphur and brimstone!" cried the Devil. "What is this?"

Before them rose a building with beautiful twin towers and three arched doorways with a flight of stone steps leading up to them. Workmen were still perched on scaffoldings around it, putting on finishing touches.

"What does this mean?" demanded the Devil. "Who has dared to put up a building without my consent?"

The Wind, looking as innocent as a spring breeze, sidled up to the Devil and murmured in his ear:

"Why doesn't your majesty go in and see?"

"I will," said the Devil. "Wait for me here."

And he stalked up the steps, pulled open the great door, and disappeared.

Now the building that the Devil went into was the famous church visited by everybody who goes to Montreal—standing on almost the same ground where, four centuries ago, a little bark chapel was lovingly built by Montreal's first settlers and called by them the Church of Our Lady, or as the French people say, the Church of Notre Dame.

I am not going to tell you what happened to the Devil in the Church of Our Lady, because I do not know. But next time you pass that way, go in and sit down in one of

216

the pews near the back. Stay there for five minutes, if you can spare the time, and see what happens to you.

The old church is very quiet. You hear nothing—except, perhaps, the gentle footfall of someone come in to worship, or like yourself to watch and listen. You cannot see much at first because the big lamps are not lighted except at service time; but presently you notice a soft golden light against the blackness of the walls and pews, the great vaulted roof, the carved pulpit that seems to hang, invisibly held, in mid-air. Through this dusky radiance colours creep out, like rich jewels in a tapestry—pictures of the Saints, of Our Lord and His Mother; shrines in carved nooks where rose-tipped candles burn for the prayers of the poor. And then you see that the whole church is full of light, and perhaps you kneel and say a prayer for yourself, for you feel that God Himself cannot be far away.

Then as you rise and come out quietly into the sunshine, you will know quite well that nothing evil could exist in that place. Where the Devil went to, nobody knows; but it is certain that he never came out the way he went in.

All this happened over a hundred years ago, and many Masses have been said in the Church of Our Lady. But people will tell you that you cannot pass the corner of Notre Dame and Saint Sulpice Street without feeling a cool breeze blowing across your face. It is the Wind, waiting for the Devil to come out.

These are the tales of Gitche Manitou, the tales told to the children who played in his garden.

But because the thoughts of Gitche Manitou are long, and go on to eternity, there are many that we have not told and many that will be told in time to come. And there are many that will never be told, because the ways of the Great Spirit are above our wisdom and his thoughts beyond our telling.

But the children of the garden know them, and they are the ones who matter.

Bibliography

SOURCE MATERIAL

Paul Radin, *Literary Aspects of North American Mythology* (Anthropological Series, Canadian Department of Mines).

M. Benjamin Sulte, *Indian Tribes of the Seventeenth Century* (Ontario Archaeological Report, 1899).

William E. Connolly, *The Wyandots* (Ontario Archaeological Report, 1899).

Charles Clay, *Swampy Cree Legends* (Macmillan).

K. B. Judson, *Myths and Legends* (A. C. McClurg).

Edward C. Woodley, *Legends of French Canada* (Nelson).

Paul Wallace, *Baptiste Larocque* (Musson).

Paul Radin, *Some Myths and Tales of the Ojibwa of Southeastern Ontario* (Anthropological Series, Canadian Department of Mines).

The Hurons (Ontario Archaeological Report, 1921-2).

Algonquin Subtribes and Clans of Ontario (Ontario Archaeological Report, 1921-2).

Bloomfield, *Sacred Stories of the Sweet Grass Cree* (Anthropological Series, Canadian Department of Mines).

Alfred Carmichael, *Indian Legends of Vancouver Island* (Musson).

E. Pauline Johnson, *Legends of Vancouver* (McClelland & Stewart).

W. R. Harris, *Parent Lands of our Algonquins and Hurons* (Ontario Archaeological Report, 1921-2).

The Baldoon Mystery (pamphlet published by *The Wallaceburg News*).

E. A. Owen, *Pioneer Sketches of Long Point* (Briggs).

G. W. Browne, *The Saint Lawrence River* (Putnam).

GENERAL READING

Dorothy Duncan, *Here's To Canada* (Harper).

Katherine Hale, *Canadian Houses of Romance* (Macmillan).

Katherine Hale, *Canadian Cities of Romance* (McClelland & Stewart).

Isabel Eccleston Mackay, *Indian Nights* (McClelland & Stewart).

Mabel Burkholder, *Before the White Man Came* (McClelland & Stewart).

Paul Kane, *Wanderings of an Artist* (Radisson Society).

Bruce Hutchison, *The Unknown Country* (Longmans Green).

Frank Oliver Call, *The Spell of French Canada* (L. C. Page & Co.).

Dorothy Hogner, *Summer Roads to Gaspé* (Dutton).

J. M. Clarke, *The Heart of Gaspé* (Macmillan).

Doris Montgomery, *The Gaspé Coast in Focus* (Dutton).

Victor Morin, *Old Montreal with Pen and Pencil* (Canadian Pacific Railway).

J. Murray Gibbon, *Canadian Folk Songs* (J. M. Dent).

Blodwen Davies, *Storied York* (Ryerson).

E. P. Weaver, *The Story of the Counties of Ontario* (Bell & Cockburn).

Wilfred Campbell, *The Canadian Lake Region* (Musson).

Dorothy Duncan, *Bluenose* (Harper).

T. Morrirs Longstreth, *To Nova Scotia* (Ryerson).

Clara Dennis, *Down in Nova Scotia* (Ryerson).

Helen Jean Champion, *Over on the Island* (Ryerson).

Stephen Leacock, *My Discovery of the West* (Allen).

David Lamson, *Once in My Saddle* (Scribner).

Emily Carr, *Klee Wyck* (Oxford University Press).

Marius Barbeau, *Indian Days in the Rockies* (Macmillan).

Gwen Cash, *I Like British Columbia* (Macmillan).

Glynn-Ward, *The Glamour of British Columbia* (Macmillan).

Sydney Montague, *North to Adventure* (McBride).

Wilfred Grenfell, *The Romance of Labrador* (Macmillan).

Philip Godsell, *The Vanished Frontier* (Ryerson).

Philip Godsell, *Red Hunters of the Snows* (Ryerson).